Bart Starr: The Cool Quarterback

About the Book

Bart Starr has quarterbacked more winning games than any other player in the history of pro football. His crisp hand-offs, quick passes, precise timing, and clever play calling have led the Green Bay Packers to six Western Conference titles, five National Football League championships, and two Super Bowl wins. Author George Sullivan tells the colorful story of Bart the Cool—the failures, frustrations, and triumphs— all the way from the muddy back lots of hometown Montgomery, Alabama, to the green turf of the Super Bowl.

BART STARR

by George Sullivan

The Cool Quarterback

G. P. Putnam's Sons

New York

Contents

1 Squeeze Play 9
2 What Kind of Quarterback Is Bart Starr? 15
3 High School Hero 23
4 Good Times and Bad 31
5 The Packers 37
6 Close Doesn't Count 49
7 Coach 67
8 "The Greatest Team" 79
9 "Back Where We Belong" 97
10 Bart Starr of Chateau Drive 115
11 Secrets of Quarterbacking 121
12 Super Bowl 139
13 Super Starr 153
14 "I'm Still Learning" 159
15 Star-Crossed Season 171
16 "The Pack Will Be Back" 183
Bart Starr's Lifetime Statistics 187
Index 188

Bart Starr: The Cool Quarterback

1
Squeeze Play

The time: the last day of December, 1967. The place: Lambeau Stadium, Green Bay, Wisconsin. The event: the game between the Packers and the Dallas Cowboys to decide the NFL championship.

GREEN BAY HAS THE BALL on the Dallas 30-yard line. Less than two minutes are left, and the Packers are behind, 17–14.

It has been a rugged day for quarterback Bart Starr. He has been dumped more times than he can count, and his body aches in a hundred places. But worse than the pain is the paralyzing cold. It is an incredible 13 degrees below zero.

Bart blows on his frozen fingers as the team huddles. Calmly, he calls a pass with Carroll Dale, the primary receiver.

He walks smartly up to the ball. He crouches over the center, and his head turns quickly left, then right as he surveys the Cowboy defense. The signals come like bursts from a machine gun: "Set . . . twenty-one . . . ninety-seven . . . hut! . . . hut! . . . hut!"

The center slaps the ball into Bart's waiting hands. He darts back, his right arm poised to throw. He sees that Dale is covered, but the linebacker covering Chuck Mercein has slipped, and Mercein is wide open. Bart fires. Perfect. Mercein eludes a tackler and races 19 yards to the Packer 11-yard line, where he is run out of bounds.

On the next play, Bart gambles. He calls a play that causes Packer guard Gale Gillingham to "pull," to vacate his normal slot and run laterally to the right, as if to lead the blocking. Bart is betting that Bob Lilly, the Cowboy tackle, will follow Gillingham's move, leaving a yawning gap in the line. Then Bart will send Chuck Mercein into the hole. But if Lilly isn't suckered out, if he doesn't take the fake and hold his ground, he'll be in a perfect position to stop Mercein dead.

The gamble pays off. Lilly streaks to his left to follow Gillingham. The hole opens up. Bart fakes to Anderson, then gives the ball to the plunging Mercein. Mercein drives to the 3-yard line.

Now there is a minute to play. Bart hands off to Anderson, who drives for a first down on the Cowboy 1. The crowd is in a frenzy.

Bart hands to Anderson again. No gain.

Bart gives to Anderson one more time. Anderson, unable to get his footing on the spongy turf, slips and goes down a yard from the end zone.

Only sixteen seconds are left. Bart calls the Packers' last time-out. He is facing the toughest yard of his life. A pass would be too risky. A field goal? It would be a cinch from this distance, tying the score, sending the game into sudden-death overtime. But Bart Starr does not want a tie. He is bound the Packers are going to win. It has to be a run.

As the team huddles, Bart's mind is racing. He rules out running to the right side, to Lilly's side. Lilly drives in too hard and low. Bart decides he will take his chances with the other Dallas tackle, Jethro Pugh.

Green Bay guard Jerry Kramer plays opposite Pugh. It will be Kramer's job to drive Pugh back. "Can you get enough footing?" Bart asks.

"I can," Kramer answers, "and I will."

Then Starr announces, "Thirty-one wedge"—a full-back plunge between center and guard. "And we darn well better make it!"

As the team breaks from the huddle, Bart is worrying that the fullback might drop the hand-off or slip on the soft ground. It has happened before. As he bends over the center and barks the signals, a thought flashes through his mind: "Run it yourself!"

"Hut! . . . Hut!" The ball slams into Bart's hands, and he tucks it to his belly. Kramer, driving off his right-foot, smashes into Jethro, driving him in and back. Starr is right behind, coming like an express bus.

As he hits the hole, Bart falls forward and stretches into the end. The referee's arms shoot over his head.

Then all hell breaks loose. The delirious fans stream down onto the field, pummeling players on the back, Packers and Cowboys alike.

Bart has to fight his way through the crowd to get to the sideline. When he comes off the field, there are tears in his eyes.

Those two minutes of that frigid day at Lambeau Stadium tell plenty about Bart Starr. First, you notice his skills—the quick, accurate passes, the crisp hand-offs, the precise timing, and clever play calling.

Much also is revealed about the man himself—his courage, his confidence, his perception, and his nimble mind.

Bart Starr is also a tough man. But it is an inner toughness. See him off the field and you realize he is as gentle as a summer breeze.

He comes at you with a quick, purposeful stride, and you notice the broad shoulders and the fact that he is tall. He stands 6 feet, 1 inch, but he looks taller because he walks rod-straight.

His brown hair is carefully combed. When he smiles, white teeth show in a face made handsome by alert, pale-blue eyes and wide cheekbones.

There is a no-nonsense look about him. You could take him for a young prosecuting attorney or a field agent for the FBI.

There is a look of success about him, too. This is fitting, for it is a matter of undisputed fact that Bart

Starr has quarterbacked more winning games than any other player in the history of pro football.

There's more. He was the league's leading passer in 1962, 1964, and 1966. He holds the league record for most consecutive passes without an interception—294. He holds the NFL record for the highest percentage of career completions—an incredible 58.8 percent.

Statistics mean very little to Bart himself. "They're important only if they're by-products of winning," he says.

Well, Bart *ha*s won.

Starr has led the Packers to six Western Conference titles and five National Football League championships, including an unprecedented feat of three play-off victories in a row. He has steered the Green Bay Packers to two Super Bowl wins in two tries against the champions of the American Football League.

Bart carries his success with singular modesty. "Humble" and "unassuming" are the words frequently used to describe him. Indeed, the niceness of Bart Starr is almost legendary, like the fact that Joe Namath swings or Mickey Mantle had bad knees. Think Bart Starr, and you think, "Nice guy."

Success did not come easily for Bart. There were years of disappointment and failure. His quarterbacking career began on the back lots of his hometown of Montgomery, Alabama. In high school he was hailed as a boy wonder, and later, as a mere freshman at the University of Alabama, he was an Orange Bowl hero. But then came a crippling injury, and Bart was consigned to the bench.

The Green Bay Packers took a chance on Bart and drafted him. In his first three years with the Packers, the team lost many more games than it won. They were years of self-doubt, bitterness, and deep frustration for Bart.

It was never easy.

The pages that follow tell it "like it happened."

2
What Kind of Quarterback Is Bart Starr?

JOHNNY UNITAS OF THE COLTS is a gifted artist, an inspired play caller, and a daring passer. Everyone knows Fran Tarkenton's leading feature; the Giants' quarterback is a scrambler. Earl Morrall of the Colts is a skilled technician and perhaps the best ball handler in the game. Milt Plum of the Giants is quarterbacking's perennial backup man.

Each player puts his own special stamp on the job of quarterbacking. What about Bart Starr? What kind of quarterback is he?

Listen to Joe Schmidt, once an All-Pro linebacker for the Detroit Lions and now the team's coach. Says Schmidt, "Bart Starr is cool out there. That's the big thing. Nothing seems to rattle him. You can never get him mad, and that's what we like to do, get the quarterback all excited and mad. You can hit Starr as hard as you want, and he never seems to lose his cool."

Bart the Cool—that's what Starr has been called by his teammates and rival players. The nickname fits.

Once during the 1967 season, Bart led the Packers into New York for an important game against the Giants. The New Yorkers grabbed a 14–7 lead. With one minute, eleven seconds left in the first half, the Packers took over the ball. How Bart performed in those seventy-one seconds makes it clearly evident why they call him Bart the Cool.

With one eye on the clock, Bart called three running plays and one pass to work the ball to the New York 14-yard line. Seven seconds remained.

Don Chandler, Green Bay's field-goal kicker, started to run out on the field. Bart waved him back. He called a pass, pitching to Boyd Dowler in the end zone, but it went incomplete.

Now there were only two seconds left. But to Bart, two seconds proved plenty of time. Out came Chandler. Bart held. The kick was good. The Packers went on to win.

What kind of quarterback is Bart Starr?

"As a play caller, Starr is Mr. Conservative." That's what you may hear. True? Consider this.

It is November, 1964, and the Packers are playing the tough Cleveland Browns, ultimate winners of the Eastern Conference, at Milwaukee County Stadium. It is the third quarter. The Packers, behind 14–7, are on their own 44-yard line. It is fourth down and inches to go for a first down. Lombardi tells Starr to go for it.

Cleveland figures that fullback Jimmy Taylor will be blasting into the line. They send their staunchest defensemen into the game, the players who man the line on goal-line defenses.

Starr gets the snap. *Thwack!* Into the line goes Taylor. The Cleveland behemoths dig in and stop him. But Taylor doesn't have the ball. Max McGee does. After faking a hand-off to Taylor, Starr flipped a short pass to McGee. By the time the Browns realize what has happened, McGee is on his way to the end zone. They finally stop him at the 1-yard line.

On the next play, the Packers tie the score. Less than five minutes later, the Packers forge ahead. Final score: Green Bay, 28; Cleveland, 21.

"That call was all Bart's," Lombardi says after the game. "He called it. We certainly didn't plan to pass from there."

"I didn't have anything to do with the call," says Max McGee. "Not me. In fact, I kind of shuddered in the huddle when Bart called it."

Bart Starr, Mr. Conservative? Not for a minute.

What kind of quarterback is Bart Starr?

It is the first Sunday in October, 1967. The Packers are playing the Atlanta Falcons in Milwaukee. It is Green Bay's ball. But Starr is on the sidelines.

Midway in the first quarter, Bart was slammed to the ground under the pressure of a fierce blitz. When he came off the field, he was clutching his right forearm, already heavily bandaged because of a previous injury.

When Bart pulls off his helmet, his face is contorted

with pain. Somebody wipes the sweat from his forehead, and the team doctor gives him a pill to swallow.

While a trainer massages his shoulder, Bart follows the action on the field. It is Green Bay's ball again, and Zeke Bratkowski, Green Bay's No. 2 quarterback and Bart's close friend, is calling the signals.

The ball is deep in Atlanta territory. Bratkowski drifts back to pass. He throws on a line to Carroll Dale in the end zone. Dale grabs it for a touchdown. Bart forgets his injury and claps his hands. His face breaks into a wide smile.

When Bratkowski comes off the field, Bart is the first to meet him at the sideline. "How to go, Zeke!" he says, and he puts out his hand.

Despite the pain of injury, despite the frustration of bench sitting, Bart Starr is still the gentleman and team player.

Ask him about this quality, and this is what he says, "Individual performances don't mean a thing on this ball club. Corny as it may sound, we're a *team*. We're honestly not concerned with personal images."

This belief of Bart's is made obvious by his personal relationships with his teammates. He is always the comrade-in-arms, never the overbearing authoritarian.

During the first half of a game against the Detroit Lions several years ago, Starr's pass protection broke down, and he was trampled on play after play. Starr never grumbled. He never said a word.

"No one feels worse about it when they miss a block than the blockers do," Starr said after the game. "When Fuzzy Thurston (Green Bay's All-Pro guard) misses Roger Brown (Detroit's defensive tackle) over and over again, there's no one in the stadium that feels worse than Fuzzy. So why chew him out? He knows it."

Green Bay center Jimmy Ringo had a different version of the incident. In a postgame interview, he said, "Bart should have been voted Most Courageous Athlete of the Year for coming out for the second half. But he never complained once. Not a word.

"Sometimes it's better to be quiet," Ringo continued. "It makes a guy feel bad when he misses a block and sees what happens to Starr."

Apparently the Green Bay blockers did feel bad for what happened to Starr. The next time the Packers played the Lions, Green Bay won with ease, and Bart's semicircle of protection was close to perfect. Only once was he knocked on his number.

Guard and author Jerry Kramer once observed that Bart seldom shows emotion during a game. "He doesn't get too excited," Kramer said. "I remember one game when we were trying to pick up momentum for a drive. Bart yelled out to me, 'C'mon, Jerry, let's go.'

"The next day he apologized for saying it."

Intelligence is another quality that Bart displays. The 1962 NFL championship game, in which Green Bay turned back the New York Giants, 16–7, featured a good example of Starr's mental acuity.

Late in the second quarter, Jimmy Taylor scored the game's first touchdown, a decisive play since it gave the Packers a 10–0 lead. The touchdown came after Phil King of the Giants fumbled on the New York

28-yard line. Green Bay linebacker Ray Nitschke recovered. Starr then handed to Hornung who threw to Boyd Dowler on the 7-yard line. Then came Taylor's run. Jimmy hit the middle, veered left, and went over without anybody touching him.

Two solid plays that seemed routine. But were they? Not at all. Plenty of reasoning, based on knowledge and experience, was involved.

Bart explained his thinking to *Sport* magazine:

> One thing I like to do after a team fumbles is to hit them right now, while they're trying to collect themselves. The option run or pass with Hornung gave us a good threat. It wasn't the straight turn and hand to Paul, where he runs a sweep or throws. I thought they might be looking for that. So I called a dive fake, sending Taylor up the middle and bringing Hornung across. It looked more like a run.

Regarding the play that followed, Starr had this to say: "The play is one of the best. It is designed to go to the right side with cross blocking up front. But we must have caught Sam Huff [the New York linebacker] guessing. Jimmy hit the line and slid left and had a clear path."

Bart is renowned for much more than his on-the-field skills. He also has one of the sport's most attractive off-the-field personalities.

Just before the 1965 season got under way, Earl Morrall of the Detroit Lions was traded to the New York Giants. It was a critical point in Morrall's career. He was thirty-one; he had been with the Lions for seven years. Would he be able to learn the signal system and catch on with the new club? Even Morrall had his doubts. Earl's first starting assignment with the Giants came in an exhibition game in Dallas. Minutes before the game, Morrall was handed a telegram. It read, "ALL OF YOUR FRIENDS HERE IN GREEN BAY JOIN ME IN WISHING YOU THE BEST TODAY AND A SUCCESFUL YEAR."

The telegram was signed, "BART STARR."

It was a thoughtful, generous act. It was one quarterback saying to another, "I know what you're going through. Give 'em hell!" Earl Morrall remembers that telegram to this day.

What kind of quarterback is Bart Starr?

Jack Christiansen, onetime coach of the San Francisco 49ers, gives the best answer. Says Christiansen, "He is probably the best quarterback in football today. And when he retires, I expect that he will be recognized as the greatest of all time."

3

High School Hero

"I'M GIVING UP FOOTBALL," the boy announced, tears welling up in his eyes.

Bart Starr's father, a master sergeant in the Air Force, knew what the problem was. His fifteen-year-old son had been assigned to the high school scrub team. He couldn't stand being a second stringer.

Sergeant Starr took his son's announcement calmly. "Okay, Bart," he said. "You can quit if you want. But tomorrow after school I want you in the garden cutting down all the corn stalks. Turn over the earth. Police up the whole area. Get it ready for winter."

Bart's father knew that his young son had no love for gardening. His psychology worked. The next afternoon Bart went back to the high school football field.

Bart, at fifteen, was of average size, and as his coach recalls, "There wasn't anything real special about the way he threw the ball.

"But he was a bright youngster and very alert. He never failed to pay attention. He'd take in every word we'd say."

In his second year at high school, Bart made the squad as the team's No. 2 quarterback. He usually played only when a game was safe in hand.

Then fate took a hand. During the fourth game of the season, the No. 1 quarterback broke his leg. "Bart," the coach said, "get in there. Now it's up to you."

The butterflies were fluttering in Bart's stomach when he sprinted out onto the field. He called a running play. Breaking from the huddle, he stepped confidently in behind the center. He called out the signals loud and clear. His nervousness had vanished. Bart the Cool his teammates were to call him in the years to come. He could have earned the name that day.

"He stepped in there," his coach said later, "and played seven ball games like you've never seen a boy play."

Led by Bart, the high school eleven whipped powerful teams from Tuscaloosa, Selma, and Dothan. In the final game of the season, they played a team from Macon, Georgia, a team with the same name as their own—Sidney Lanier High School.

The team's quarterback was a master at bootlegging. He'd hide the ball on his hip after taking the snap from center. Sometimes he would hand off to the halfback, while other times he'd run the ball himself or pass. He bewildered the opposition with his magic.

The game was close. Late in the third quarter, Bart maneuvered Lanier downfield.

He had been studying the enemy quarterback. Now he decided to put into use what he had learned.

He took the snap from center, then tucked the ball against his leg. He gave his halfback an empty hand, then rolled to the right, the ball still hidden.

"He's going to pass!" a fan screamed. "No!" said another. "He's going to run!"

The enemy team was just as puzzled as the fans. By the time they realized what was happening, it was too late.

Bart spotted a receiver deep in the end zone and tossed him a feathery floater. The man gathered it in. Touchdown!

Bart's team went on to win the game, closing out an undefeated season. Bart Starr never played as a scrub again.

Bryan Bartlett Starr was born in Montgomery, Alabama, on January 9, 1934. Bryan was his father's middle name. Bartlett was the surname of the doctor who delivered him, a close family friend. At first his parents called him Bryan, but Bart was the name that caught on.

Bart's father, Benjamin Bryan Starr, had been a sure-fingered end in high school. He had also boxed.

When young Bart began to toddle about the house, his father gave him a tiny rubber football. As Bart grew, the footballs kept getting bigger.

Soon Bart was running, passing, and kicking in the

backyard. His father showed Bart and his brother, Hilton, two years younger than Bart, how to catch and how to throw the ball.

"Your hand is small," his father said to Bart. "So hold the ball away back. Don't try to grip the laces. Get your thumb into a seam."

Bart remembers his boyhood fondly. "My family always encouraged me in whatever I was doing," he once said, "whether it was football, baseball, or anything else. My dad always had time for me."

From backyard practice sessions, Bart moved to vacant corner lots. He and his friends would gather together after school or on Saturdays and play until dark.

A tragedy marred Bart's boyhood. One summer when Bart was twelve, he and Hilton were playing hide-and-seek barefoot. Hilton stepped on a jagged piece of bone that tore a gash in his foot. Although he received medical treatment, the boy contracted tetanus and died.

After Hilton's death, Bart felt a terrible emptiness. "We had a lot of fun together," Bart has said. "After he died, I felt a real vacuum, a gap. I hope this doesn't sound corny, but I've dedicated myself many times since then striving to do something for him."

In Bart's boyhood days, there was little opportunity to play organized football. There were no Pop Warner Leagues or Tiger Leagues as there are today.

But Bart was lucky enough to play with a team sponsored by the Veterans of Foreign Wars in Montgomery. Everyone who made the team received a uniform. "This was one of the real milestones in our lives," Bart says.

At Baldwin Junior High School, Bart played tailback in a variation of the single wing formation known as the Notre Dame box. He handled the ball on almost every play, and liked it.

"He wasn't a big boy and he wasn't particularly fast," his coach recalls. "But somehow when he got his hands on the ball, he got big yardage, ten and twenty yards at a whack. He did it time and time again."

When Bart entered Sidney Lanier High School, he ran into difficulty. The team was using the T formation. There is no tailback in the T formation. Bart decided to become a quarterback. It was not easy to make the switch, one reason why Bart was assigned to the scrubs during his freshman year.

Bart spent long hours on the practice field and in meetings with head coach Bill Moseley. His brainpower impressed the coach. "You'd explain a play to him once, and he'd be able to run through it perfectly," Moseley recalls. "And he was the kind of boy you could sit down with and map out a whole new series of offensive plays. He was that smart."

Bart had a brilliant senior year, and he was named to the All-American High School Team. The Lanier team lost only one game.

The highlight of the season was a trip to Louisville to play one of the toughest high school teams in the Southeast, Louisville's Manual High. The team was known for its ferocious pass rush. It was to be a stiff test for Bart.

Early in the game, Bart drifted back to pass. The blitz was on, and the tacklers came bursting in. Bart proved as elusive as a cake of soap in the bathtub. He slipped from one man's grasp and then another's.

Bart scampered toward the sideline, hulking linemen in pursuit. Bart seemed not to notice them as he searched for an open man.

Then Bart found a target. He cocked his arm. A tackler made a dive for him. Bart sidestepped, and the man flew past. As cool as an iceberg, Bart fired. Perfect. Twenty yards downfield, the ball arched into the arms of a receiver.

Bart was masterful that day. Lanier won by twenty points.

After the game, college scouts by the score contacted Bart. They came from New England and from every part of the South. They came from as far away as California.

Bart, however, had already set his mind on attending one of two schools—the University of Kentucky or the University of Alabama. Each one had offered him a scholarship.

For a time Bart thought he might choose Kentucky. The team was coached by Bear Bryant, a man of legendary fame.

During the summer just before Bart's senior year in high school, Bryant invited Bart to the Kentucky campus at Lexington. There he met Kentucky's All-American quarterback, Vito "Babe" Parilli, and stayed for two weeks.

"I learned more from Parilli in those two weeks than

anyone had taught me in my life," Bart was to say in later years. "No one could fake more deceptively than Babe. He taught me fundamentals that I still practice."

Another of Bart's idols was flashy Harry Gilmer, the jump-passing Alabama quarterback of the late 1940's. As a daring eighteen-year-old, Gilmer had quarterbacked Alabama in the Sugar Bowl game of 1945. He also starred for the Crimson Tide in the Rose Bowl in 1946 and the Sugar Bowl in 1948. Gilmer then went on to a nine-year career in professional football.

Bart would have loved to follow in Gilmer's footsteps, but he couldn't make up his mind. Kentucky or Alabama? Kentucky or Alabama? The question haunted him. Then something happened, and suddenly it wasn't a difficult decision anymore.

Pretty, dark-haired Cherry Morton, Bart's high school sweetheart, told him that she was going to Auburn University, in Auburn, Alabama. This news started Bart thinking. "If I pick Kentucky, I'm going to be an awful long way from Cherry. She could meet another boy. But if I choose Alabama, I won't be too far away."

Bart Starr decided he would go to Alabama.

4

Good Times and Bad

It is New Year's Day, 1953, and Alabama's Crimson Tide is rolling to an easy victory over Syracuse at the Orange Bowl in Miami, Florida. Late in the game, Coach Red Drew sends a boyish-faced freshman named Bart Starr into the game to direct the team.

Starr is calm and confident. He mixes his plays like a veteran. He passes with pinpoint accuracy. Of the twelve passes he tries, he completes eight, and one, a 22 yarder, is caught in the end zone for a touchdown.

The largest crowd in the history of the Orange Bowl sends up a thunderous roar of approval as the referee stretches his arms into the air. The touchdown breaks the record for the most points ever scored by one team in the Orange Bowl. Bart Starr, only eighteen years old, is hailed as a hero.

The next year brought more of the same. As the team's No. 1 quarterback, Bart led Alabama to the

Southeastern Conference championship and then took the team to the Cotton Bowl.

If there was one thing that marked Bart's winning performances during this period, it was his accuracy as a passer. In his sophomore season, he completed 59 out of 119 passes for 870 yards. Remarkably, only 6 were intercepted. Eight tosses went for touchdowns, the most thrown by any passer in the Conference.

Experts were saying that Bart Starr was the best quarterback in Alabama history, even better than Harry Gilmer.

Then came a turning point, the beginning of a long downhill slide. There were days filled with bitter anguish and burning disappointment. There were months, even years, as bleak and cheerless as a winter day.

The change in Bart's fortune began innocently enough. Bart was Alabama's punter. (In 1953 he averaged 41 yards a kick, second best in the nation that year.) One sun-filled August day in 1954, Bart was getting himself in shape at the practice field at the University of Alabama.

He boomed kick after kick far downfield. Ready to try again, he picked up a ball. He held it in front of his body, dropped it, then took a powerful stride forward, swinging his right leg into the ball. When he did, something in Bart's back snapped. The sudden pain made him wince.

A teammate was watching. "You all right, Bart?" he asked. Bart nodded. "It's just a kink in my back," he said. "I'll work it out."

He kicked another ball and another and kept on through the afternoon. That night his back hurt so much he had trouble sleeping.

Bart continued practicing, trying to "work it out." But within the next few days, the pain became so intense that he couldn't bend over far enough to tie his shoelaces.

He went to see a doctor, who ordered X rays. "Your sacroiliac has slipped out of position," the doctor told Bart.

Then he explained that the sacroiliac is a joint in the spinal column at the base of the back. Should the sacroiliac slip out of place, the strained nerves send flashes of pain into the arms and legs.

Bart did not need a doctor to tell him that. The pain had become so great he could not raise his right arm high enough to hail a cab. Trying to pass a football was out of the question.

Bart missed the first three games of the season. The pain would not subside. Finally the doctors persuaded him to enter a hospital for treatment. When he was released, he managed to play in a few games, but never on a full-time basis.

"It was a messed-up season for me," Bart says. Indeed it was.

By the fall of the next year, Bart had recovered. He felt ready for a banner season.

But Bart's struggle with bad fortune was just beginning.

The year before had been as disappointing for Alabama as it had been for Bart, and coach Harold "Red"

Drew had resigned. J. B. "Ears" Whitworth, the head coach at Oklahoma A & M, was named to replace Drew.

Whitworth had grand plans. "I want to start fresh," he told an assistant. "We're going to rebuild right from the bottom. Those veteran players may have gotten into the habit of losing. We're going to play the younger fellows."

When the season opened, the seniors were on the bench. And Bart was a senior.

It is bad enough to sit on the bench when you are injured. You feel you are no longer part of the team. It is worse, much worse, to sit on the bench when you are in good health. It can be heartbreaking.

Bart didn't start a single game during his senior year. Once, when the opposition had built up a commanding lead early in the game, Whitworth put Bart in. On the third play from scrimmage, he sprained his ankle and limped off the field.

In his book, *Quarterbacking*, Bart called the season ". . . a living hell. I was never so glad in all my life to get a season behind me."

It was equally as disappointing for the team as a whole. Whitworth's strategy of relying upon sophomores and juniors was a wholesale failure. Alabama played ten games that season. They lost all ten.

Bart, as a bench sitter, was hardly noticed by scouts from the National Football League. When the season was over and pro team representatives assembled for the annual player draft, they spoke in glowing terms of Howard "Hopalong" Cassady, the brilliant running back from Ohio State, Don Chandler, the University of Florida's vaunted kicker, Dick Szymanski, Notre Dame's All-American center, and Earl Morrall, the quarterback whose ball-handling magic had helped make Michigan State the No. 1 team in the country.

Bart Starr? Many of the team representatives had never heard of him.

However, Johnny Dee, the basketball coach at Alabama, happened to be one man who thought highly of Bart's skills. While at Notre Dame, Dee had made friends with one Jack Vainisi. After graduation, Vainisi became business manager of the Green Bay Packers.

Just before the player draft, Dee told Vainisi, "Pick up Bart Starr. He's a good one."

Despite Dee's tip, Green Bay was in no hurry to draft Bart. They waited until the seventeenth round, until 198 other players had been picked. Bart's selection was a wild gamble, a hope that a sleeper might come through.

Bart was delighted when he learned he had been drafted. He needed a boost.

The dreadful year at Alabama had robbed Bart of much of his confidence. He was down as low as he had ever been in his life.

Although others had given up on him, Bart would not give up on himself. More than anything else in the world, he now wanted to make the Green Bay team, and he set out to accomplish this objective with deadly determination.

5
The Packers

GREEN BAY, WISCONSIN, with a population of 82,-472, is unlike any other small city in the United States because it has its own football team. It is just as anomalous as Pontiac, Michigan, or Stockton, California, having a major league baseball franchise.

Naturally, the citizens of Green Bay regard their team in a special way. Whereas the Bears are merely popular in Chicago, and the Giants only revered in New York, the Packers absolutely dominate life in Green Bay.

For years, the only way a fan has been able to see a game from the tiered benches at Lambeau Stadium has been to buy a season ticket. And whether the team has been winning or losing, it takes years of waiting to get one.

Color portraits of Packer players look down from the walls of soda fountains and stare up from restaurant windows. Signs proclaiming "We're Packer Back-ers" are everywhere.

Virtually every youngster has a Packer autograph book. There is a good chance he drinks his milk from a Packer souvenir glass, saves small change in a Packer football bank, and protects his school books with Pack-er covers. It is likely that on his bedroom dresser there stands a small Packer mascot doll with a head that waggles.

The pastors of some Green Bay churches have been known to end their Sunday sermons with a short, solemn prayer for the team's success. When the Pack is playing on the road and the game is televised in Green Bay, the streets become silent and deserted, and the city remains a ghost town right up to the final commer-cial.

Green Bay's love of the Packers has been going on for a very long time. On the evening of August 11, 1919, a husky young man with a fiery spirit by the name of Curly Lambeau called a meeting of several broad-shouldered young men, all former high school or college players. Sitting on chairs and desktops in the newsroom of the Green Bay *Press-Gazette*, they heard Lambeau propose they organize a semipro football team. They all loved the sport. It sounded like a fine idea.

"But where will we get the money to pay for the uniforms?" someone asked.

Lambeau had the answer. "I'll try the company I work for, the Indian Packing Company."

Curly's employer agreed to put up $500 to outfit the

team. In return, the company asked that the team jerseys bear the name "Indian Packing Co." It was natural for the fans to shorten the name to "Packers."

Home games were played at Green Bay's Hagemeister Park. There were no fences and no stands. The playing field was a roped-off area, and the fans, most of whom got to the park by trolley car, ringed the gridiron. When the game got exciting, they often spilled out onto the field itself.

Instead of collecting an admission charge, a helmet was passed through the crowd, and the fans made contributions. At the end of the first season when the profits were distributed, each player got $16.75.

In 1921, the Packers joined the newly formed National Football League. Other teams of the time included the Decatur Staleys, the Chicago Cardinals, the Canton Bulldogs, and the Columbus Panhandlers. Of all the league's original members, only the Packers are playing in the city in which they were founded.

Survival was a grim struggle, however. In 1921 the team's franchise was revoked for using college players under assumed names. But Lambeau organized new backers and bought back the franchise.

Money to operate the team was always in short supply. Time and again the businessmen of Green Bay came to the club's rescue. In 1923, when the team was in serious financial trouble, fifty community leaders each pledged $100 to forestall failure.

Almost from the beginning, shares of stock in the club were sold to the public, a tradition that continues

to this day. About 1,700 Green Bay citizens—
salesmen, factory workers, and grocery store clerks—
own shares in the Packers. They understand that no
dividends are to be paid, that any profits will be used in
further developing the team.

Once he had established a firm financial base, Lambeau was able to devote more time to developing a
top-flight team. In 1929 his efforts paid off as the
Packers won the championship of the National Football League. They repeated in 1930 and 1931. No
team had ever won three consecutive championships
before.

Financial woes struck the club again in 1933. A fan
fell from the stands and was injured. He sued and was
awarded $5,000. The judgment helped push Green
Bay into bankruptcy. But again the local businessmen
and the public came forth with fresh money to save the
club.

The immortal Don Hutson, one of the greatest pass
receivers pro football has ever known, was a feature of
the Packer attack during the late 1930's. All types of
defenses were used to stop Hutson, but they met with
almost universal failure. Green Bay won the Western
Division championship in 1935, 1938, and 1939, and
the NFL crown in 1936 and 1938.

The pro football war between the National League
and the All-America Conference caused the Packers
another financial crisis in the late 1940's. This time the
storm triggered Lambeau's resignation. Gene Ronzani
was brought in to coach the team. For a time the

Packers showed improvement, but in 1953 they nose-dived to last place in the Western Conference with a 2-9-1 record. Ronzani resigned.

The third coach in Green Bay history was Lisle "Liz" Blackbourn. His experience included twenty-two years as a high school coach and short periods as backfield coach at the University of Wisconsin and later as head coach at Marquette University.

Blackbourn handled the Green Bay players skillfully during his first year. Team performance improved, and hopes began to rise again. This was the situation in the summer of 1956 when Bryan Bartlett Starr arrived upon the scene.

Painfully shy at the time, Starr, as one observer recalls, "spent more time looking at the tops of his shoes than into people's eyes." Few believed he would ever make the grade in the National Football League.

Bart began to have trouble with his back again not long after he arrived at the Packers' training camp. "He was in such bad shape," Blackbourn recalls, "there was some question how much help he would be to us."

Dr. Frederick Reichardt, the team doctor, suggested that the punting that Bart was doing might be causing his back problem. "Lay off the kicking for a while," Blackbourn told Bart.

Bart quit punting. His back troubles disappeared.

The heavy competition Bart encountered in training camp was another problem. There were no less than four other quarterbacks on hand. No team ever carries more than three.

Yet Bart did make the squad. There were, however, many anxious moments. "Until the final cut," he was to say later, "I was never sure I was going to make the club. When I knew I had, it was one of the happiest moments of my life."

A rookie quickly finds that there is a sharp difference between college and pro football. It is not easy to make the switch. There is an age difference, often a six- or seven-year gap between the newcomer and the established players.

And whereas on a college team, there may be two or three soft spots, in the pros every single player is skilled. The men are bigger, stronger, and faster. And when they hit, they hit harder, much harder.

A rookie can be overwhelmed by all this. Bart wasn't. There are two important reasons why Bart managed to stick with the Packers.

First of all, he was in excellent physical shape when he arrived in camp. Sometimes rookies aren't. Occasionally a college All-American has a puffed-up idea of his importance. "I'm an All-American, a star," he figures. "I can beat out those other guys with no trouble."

He arrives in camp overweight, out of shape. He is far behind everyone else, and he never catches up. He's cut within just a few weeks.

Bart's attitude was just the opposite. He knew he would be rusty from spending so much time on the bench during his college senior year. So in the weeks before he left for the Green Bay training camp, he conducted a training program of his own.

Bart had married Cherry Morton, and the two were staying with Cherry's folks in Macon, Mississippi. Bart took some lumber and built an A-shaped frame, and from the center bar he suspended an old automobile tire. He set up the odd-looking structure on the Morton's front lawn.

Day after day in the broiling Mississippi sun, Bart threw footballs at the tire. Cherry retrieved them. "I'm sure," Bart now says, "that this concentrated work enabled me to make the Packer team."

There was a second factor. Veteran Tobin Rote was the Packers' No. 1 quarterback. Instead of looking upon young Bart as a threat to his job, a rival, Rote treated Bart the way an older brother might.

A rookie is often something of an outsider at a pro football training camp. The veteran players usually stick together. Sometimes they haze the new men, make fun of them.

When fun-loving Bobby Layne quarterbacked the Detroit Lions, rookie players were ridiculed without mercy. If a newcomer happened to make a mistake on the playing field, Layne, using language that is not printable, would bawl him out in front of the entire squad. Sometimes Layne would banish the rookie from the field.

But Bart was spared this type of treatment. Rote and his wife often invited the Starrs to dinner. They made them feel that they were among friends.

Bart roomed with Rote, and the older man would give him playing tips. John Davaney, a previous biographer of Starr's, reported that the first thing Rote said to the young rookie was, "Kid, you've got to learn to zip the ball a little. You won't make it in this league throwing cream puffs!"

Dave Hanner was another veteran player who took a special interest in Bart. A defensive left tackle and, at thirty-three, the eldest member of the team, Hanner chatted with Bart almost every night to help keep him from getting homesick.

Rookie quarterbacks seldom get to play very much in the National Football League, and Bart was no exception. His first season with the Packers went not unlike his last year at college in that he spent a great deal of time on the bench.

Blackbourn used Bart in place of Rote only when a game was hopelessly lost. Bart threw only forty-four passes for the season. He continued to be remarkably accurate with the ball, hitting on 54.5 percent of his throws. He was intercepted only three times.

It was a dreary year for the team as a whole. They finished with a 4–8 record and in a tie with Los Angeles for last place in the Western Conference.

Before the 1957 season opened, Blackbourn traded Rote to Detroit. To replace him, he brought in Babe Parilli, whom Bart had first met on the University of Kentucky campus years before.

The year 1957 also brought one other rival for the quarterbacking spot—Paul Hornung. A widely hailed All-American and winner of the Heisman Trophy, Hornung was regarded as the best college player in the country.

Blackbourn used Hornung as quarterback on third-down and short-yardage situations. He also played him at halfback and fullback. He couldn't seem to make up his mind about what to do with the talented "Golden Boy."

Blackbourn was also indecisive about the other quarterback candidates. Sometimes he used Parilli as the No. 1 man. Other times Bart was No. 1. It was like a game of musical chairs.

By mid-season the Packers had dropped out of contention for the title. Many players had developed an I-don't-give-a-damn attitude.

The team ended with a 3–9 record and in sole possession of last place.

After the season was over, the Packers asked Blackbourn to resign. He would not, so they fired him.

Blackbourn then made plans to return to Marquette University. Before leaving Green Bay, he spoke to Bart.

"You're going to have a tough time making it as a pro quarterback," he said.

Bart shrugged.

"But you learn fast," Blackbourn continued. "You understand the game's offense and defense. You'd make a fine backfield coach. Would you like to come to Marquette with me?"

Bart didn't hesitate in answering. "No, thank you, Liz," he said. "I'm going to stick it out here. I still think I can make it as a pro quarterback."

The Packers named Ray "Scooter" McLean as the new head coach. Mild-mannered and soft-spoken, McLean had been the Packers' backfield coach under

Blackbourn. A Packer official explained why McLean had been promoted: "The people of Green Bay decided to give Scooter a chance because he's such a nice guy."

Sometimes "nice guy" coaches find the going difficult. McLean did.

"The players will be on their honor," McLean announced. "They have set up a committee and will have their own system of fines for discipline."

Many players took advantage of the easygoing McLean. The season was a horror. There must have been many times when Bart wished he had gone to Marquette with Liz Blackbourn. He suffered one nightmare Sunday afternoon after another.

In a game against the Lions, Bart had completed nineteen of thirty-one passes, including five in a row, and seemed to have the team on the road to a rare win. But he suffered an ankle injury late in the game and had to go to the sidelines. The game ended in a tie.

One afternoon against the Colts, Bart was intercepted four times. Against the Bears, he was hit for losses that totaled 50 yards. Once the hard-charging Bear line flattened Bart in the end zone. He fumbled, and the Bears got a touchdown.

It is a season that Bart would like to forget but can't. There were players whose only thought was "to take care of No. 1," that is, they played only for themselves. There were other players who didn't care at all. And there were a handful, like Bart, who wanted to play, who wanted to win, but were unable to.

The team finished with a 1-10-1 record, the worst

ever in Green Bay history. And Green Bay has a very long history.

The terrible failure weighed heaviest on Bart. He realized that as No. 2 man behind Rote in 1956, and as an alternate with Parilli in 1957 and 1958, he had not directed the Packers in a single winning game.

Bart went home that winter a very discouraged young man. He had failed in college. He had failed in the pros, he believed. He doubted whether he could succeed in anything.

Once the desire to be a success had burned brightly within him. Now the flame was dying.

Bart Starr's career was at a desperate low point. He felt it could not go any lower.

6

Close Doesn't Count

WHILE STARR LICKED HIS WOUNDS during the winter of 1958–1959, Packer officials in Green Bay were interviewing coaching candidates.

But the search ran into difficulty. The men whom the Packers wanted weren't interested in the Packers, and the men who wanted the job, the Packers didn't want.

Finally, almost in desperation, the club directors settled upon a little-known assistant coach with the New York Giants, a short, stocky stump of a man, with eyes that smoldered from behind horn-rimmed glasses. His name, of course, was Vince Lombardi.

A militant leader, Lombardi signed a five-year contract as both coach and general manager, on the condition that he be in complete command, have almost unlimited authority.

Green Bay would never be the same. Neither would Bart Starr.

Bart knew immediately that things were going to be different under Lombardi. The first meeting he held was proof of that. Lombardi talked about winning right from the start.

"I've never been a losing coach," Lombardi declared. "I don't intend to start here." Bart noticed that he spoke slowly, clearly, and without effort. His voice was deep and husky. It made Bart think of a drill sergeant's voice. You could tell that Lombardi meant business.

Lombardi continued. "There is nobody here big enough to think he's got this team made or can do what he wants. Trains and planes are coming in and going out of Green Bay every hour of every day, and he'll be on one of them.

"I'm going to find thirty-six men who have the pride to make any sacrifice to win. There are such men. If they are not here, I will find them. If you are not one of those men, if you don't want to sacrifice to win, you might as well leave now."

This was a man of authority, a man of strength. Every player in the room got the message.

In their first meeting, Bart did not make a favorable impression upon Lombardi. Starr, who had been brought up on Air Force bases and other military installations, sprinkled his conversations with the word "sir." He addressed all his elders as mister.

In his book *Run to Daylight!* Lombardi says, "When I first met him, he struck me as so polite and so self-effacing that I wondered if maybe he wasn't too nice a boy to be the authoritarian leader that your quarterback must be."

Lombardi knew what the book was on Bart. Bart was said to be skilled in throwing short passes but weak on long ones. It was also being said that Bart wasn't tough enough, that he lacked confidence.

During his first weeks as the Packers' coach, Lombardi ran and reran the films of the eighteen previous Packer games. The Bart Starr he saw in those films confirmed what people were saying. The young man's confidence seemed to be at a zero point.

Lombardi did what he felt he had to do. He made a trade to get a new quarterback. He was known to be a moody young man, but he had all the tools. His name was Lamar McHan.

How did Bart feel about the trade? "I don't blame Lombardi for bringing in Lamar," Bart confessed to a friend. "The Packers need a quarterback. I haven't been doing the job, and now it looks like I never will."

When the 1959 season got under way, McHan was Green Bay's No. 1 quarterback. Bart was the No. 2 man. Joe Francis, a second-year player, was No. 3.

In the first game of what later was to be called Green Bay's Lombardi Era, McHan led the Packers to a stunning upset over the Chicago Bears. Hornung and Jimmy Taylor, with their bull-like rushes and powerful sweeps, provided the driving force.

The next week McHan fired four touchdown passes, and Green Bay beat Detroit, 28–10. The following Sunday San Francisco fell, 21–20.

Three games, three victories. Green Bay was in a state of wild excitement. Through the two previous seasons the Packers had won only six times.

Then the bubble burst. Green Bay lost five in a row.

One of those games is deeply etched in Bart's memory. The Packers were scheduled to play the Giants in New York. McHan had injured his shoulder. Nevertheless, Lombardi gave him the starting assignment. McHan's passes were constantly off target, and he could not move the team. Someone was going to have to replace him. Bart was tingling with excitement. Now I'm going to get a chance to show Coach Lombardi what I can do, he thought.

New York had the ball. Lombardi called Joe Francis over to where he was standing, then started giving him instructions. Bart knew what was about to happen. Lombardi was going to put Francis in the lineup. But wasn't he the No. 2 quarterback? Why should the No. 3 man get this chance?

Bart stared down at his lap. He hoped his shock and disappointment didn't show. "I'm better than Joe Francis," he thought. "I know I am."

Joe Francis did not have a good day. Pass after pass went awry, and the team was in trouble most of the afternoon. A field goal was their only score. They lost, 20–3.

It was a long afternoon for Bart Starr. He sat on the bench, an almost unnoticed figure, scuffing the ground with his cleats and pounding his fist into his hand.

Bart Starr does not drink—normally. But that night, in an effort to ease the deep emotional pain, he and

Rod Kramer, who didn't get into the game either, drowned their sorrows. And then they walked shadowy streets for long hours, hoping to shed their despair at being ignored.

After that calamitous afternoon in New York, Lombardi did not start Joe Francis again. He went back to McHan. The team lost to Chicago a second time, 28–17.

The next Sunday against Baltimore the Packers were being whipped, 20–3, at half time. Lombardi made two important changes.

The team had been using a backfield system that consisted of a quarterback and three running backs. Most pro teams of the time used two running backs plus a flanker—a back split wide, 6 or 8 yards outside the tight end, to receive passes.

In the locker room between halves of the Baltimore game, Lombardi said he was doing away with the three-back system. He put in a 6-foot, 5-inch 225-pound rookie named Boyd Dowler as flanker.

Lombardi had one other announcement. "Starr," he said, "you're going in as quarterback."

Bart was never better. He hit Jimmy Taylor with a touchdown pass and connected eight times with Boyd Dowler.

Baltimore won the game, but the Packers looked like a different team with Bart in the lineup. They had enthusiasm; they had punch.

Lombardi started Bart in the next four games, the final four games of the 1959 season. They beat Washington, a game in which Bart threw two touchdown passes. They then turned back Detroit and Los Angeles.

The last game of the season was against the San Francisco 49ers. That afternoon everything fell in place for Bart.

He riddled the San Francisco defenses with his pinpoint passing. He threw twenty-five times; incredibly, he completed twenty. And when he felt the 49ers were expecting a pass, he'd send Paul Hornung sluicing up the middle or careening around an end. The Pack won easily.

After the game, which earned Green Bay a third-place tie in the Western Conference, Lombardi congratulated the players individually.

His passing success, the team's four straight wins, Lombardi's kind words—they made Bart feel good inside. He felt like a pro. He felt as if he belonged. He could hardly wait for the next season to begin.

Lombardi, however, was still not sold on Starr. Before the 1960 season opened, he made it clear to the press that the Packers had *two* skilled quarterbacks—Starr and McHan.

"I don't know who will be number one" Lombardi told the two men. "I'm going to alternate you in pre-season games. Whoever moves the team the best will be the number one man."

Green Bay roared through the exhibition season, winning all six of its games. Bart was the man who looked the best. When the Packers opened the season, he was the team's quarterback.

The tough Chicago Bears were the Packers' first

opponents of the season. City Stadium in Green Bay was jammed to the rafters. When Bart's name was announced as starting quarterback, they let out a tumultuous roar.

After three quarters, the Packers led, 14–0. Then suddenly lightning struck. The Bears' Willie Galimore galloped 18 yards for a touchdown, and Rick Casares sprinted 26 yards for another. Then, with only three seconds left, Chicago kicked a field goal. Green Bay had lost, 17–14.

Lombardi started McHan in the next three games. But whenever the Green Bay attack bogged down, he would send in Bart. The Packers won all three games.

Lombardi knew his two-quarterback system would not work indefinitely, that soon he was going to have to decide who was to be his No. 1 man. Shuttling quarterbacks in and out is not a good practice, a fact almost all coaches are aware of. The two rivals become tense and overcautious, afraid to take a chance. Each realizes that if he makes a mistake, he is likely to be benched in favor of the other. To be successful, a quarterback has to be able to freewheel. He has to gamble once in a while to keep the opposition off balance. Neither Starr nor McHan felt confident enough to do this.

Of course, teams carry more than one quarterback, usually two. But in virtually every case one of the men has the starting role, while the other is strictly a backup man. He stands ready to take over in case the No. 1 man should be injured.

Lombardi was about ready to stop platooning

McHan and Starr. A game in Pittsburgh hurried his decision.

McHan started, but he couldn't put together a touchdown drive. A few of his passes were dropped.

Early in the third quarter, Lombardi sent in Starr. Immediately the team perked up. Jim Taylor scored a fourth-period touchdown, and the Packers won, 19–13.

McHan was bitter because he had been taken out in favor of Starr. "How come those guys drop my passes and hold on to his?" he asked. He made no secret of the fact that he was fed up with the two-platoon system, that he wouldn't mind being traded.

McHan's words reached Lombardi's ears. As soon as the team returned to Green Bay, Lombardi acted. He called Starr into his office.

Bart settled into a chair opposite Lombardi's desk and waited respectfully for the coach to begin. "Bart," Lombardi began, "I've made up my mind. You're my No. 1 quarterback. Win or lose, you've got the job for the rest of the year."

Lombardi had seen Bart's confidence grow game by game. He realized that Bart was a skilled technician and that he had the potential to become an inspiring leader as well. Lombardi's meeting with Starr was meant to point Bart in that direction.

The Colts had been champions of the Western Conference for two consecutive years. As the 1960 season reached its final stages, it appeared as if Baltimore was

going to win a third time. The Western Conference
standings—won, lost, and tied—looked like this:

Baltimore	6-3
Chicago	5-3-1
San Francisco	5-4
Green Bay	5-4

The Packers then faced the Bears in Chicago. It
started out as a rugged defensive battle. Each time
Bart came up to the line of scrimmage, he studied the
Chicago defenses carefully. Before very long, he could
"read" how each man was going to move.

Early in the third quarter, Green Bay had the ball
deep in Bear territory. It was second down and seven.
Bart called a pass with Max McGee, the primary
receiver. Paul Hornung was to swing to the right,
acting as a safety valve.

The team broke from the huddle. Bart stood over
the center ready to bark out the signals. Then he
spotted a flaw in the Bear defense. The linebacker who
was supposed to be covering Hornung was playing off
him. "That guy's going to be blitzing in here," Bart
thought.

Immediately Bart checked off, called a different
play. Hornung got the message.

The ball was snapped. In blasted the Chicago linebacker. Out flew Hornung, right into the spot the
linebacker had vacated.

Hornung turned. The throw was perfect. Hornung

galloped into the end zone. The play broke the game wide open. The final score was Green Bay, 41; Chicago, 13.

The win pushed the Packers ahead of the Bears in the Conference standings. But Baltimore still led.

In the gleeful Green Bay locker room, a newspaperman whispered to Lombardi, "The Lions just beat the Colts, twenty to fifteen." Now the Packers were tied with the Colts for first place.

"Are you sure?" Lombardi asked the newsman. "I don't want to tell the players unless you're positive."

"I saw it come over the ticker," the newsman said.

Lombardi stood on a stool, called for attention, and then announced what had happened. "Now we're tied with the Colts for first place." Wild cheers rang out.

Each team had two games remaining. Both were against the same two teams—the San Francisco 49ers and the Los Angeles Rams.

The next week it was raining in San Francisco, and the field was a sea of mud. Bart could do little passing. He turned to Paul Hornung, who sloshed through the goo for one touchdown and booted two field goals. The Packers won, 13–0.

The next day the Colts lost, 10–3, to the Rams. Now the Packers were undisputed leaders of the Western Conference, and only the Los Angeles Rams stood between them and the title.

A few hours before the game with the Rams, the Packers boarded the team bus outside their hotel. Precisely at the appointed departure time, an assistant coach checked his watch, then said to the driver, "Okay. Let's go."

"Hold it!" came the voice of a player from the rear of the bus. "Starr's not here yet. And neither is Knafelc."

The coach looked from seat to seat. Indeed, it was true. Neither Bart nor his room-mate, end Gary Knafelc, were aboard. Then he saw the pair racing down the street toward the bus. They jumped aboard.

Now Lombardi was on his feet and shouting. "That'll cost you twenty-five dollars each," his voice rang out.

Bart nodded, his eyes avoiding the coach's. He knew every eye was on him, and he could feel his face turning crimson.

He quickly took a seat. The bus coughed to a start. Bart sat quietly. He knew that punctuality was a passion with Lombardi. He knew that he had been wrong, that he, the supposed team leader, had delayed the bus.

But Bart did not sulk or become morose. By the time the bus pulled up to the stadium, the game was the only subject that occupied his mind.

Los Angeles scored first and took a 7–0 lead, but Bart brought the Packers roaring back like a forest fire through a canyon. He threw a 57-yard pass to Max McGee for one touchdown, and then, teaming with Boyd Dowler, worked a 91-yard pass-and-run play for another score. The Packers led 28–7 at the half and then coasted to a 35–31 win.

Now the Packers were the Western Conference champions. The plane trip home was pure joy. Despite a bitter wind and below-freezing temperatures, more than 10,000 fans were on hand to greet the team at Austin Staubel Airport. Bands played, and the crowd cheered.

The Green Bay *Press-Gazette* put out an extra edition to celebrate the Packers' first divisional championship in sixteen years. The 14,000 copies were snapped up in the blink of an eye.

In 1960, the National Football League championship was decided in a game that matched the Western Conference champion and the Eastern Conference titlist, just as today. This was at a time before the Super Bowl, however, so most observers looked upon the NFL title as being tantamount to the pro football championship.

The Philadelphia Eagles won the Eastern Conference in 1960. Norm Van Brocklin, their artful quarterback, spearheaded the Philadelphia attack. The Eagles' brilliant defensive unit was led by veteran linebacker Chuck Bednarik, a devastating tackler.

The Packers were not able to get a great deal of practice for the game because the field in Green Bay was frozen solid. But they studied films of previous Eagle games and listened to the recommendations of their coaches. The game plan called for them to emphasize a running attack.

The team flew to Philadelphia on Saturday, December 24, and held a brief workout Christmas Day. On Monday every seat in ancient Franklin Field was filled. The day dawned cold and dreary, but by game time the temperature had risen into the high thirties. This made the field soft on top, but it remained frozen underneath—treacherous going for the Green Bay backs.

The Packers kicked off, and on the first play from scrimmage, Green Bay's Bill Quinlan intercepted a Van Brocklin lateral and fell to the ground on the Eagle 14. Starr called three running plays that got the ball to the Philadelphia 6. On fourth and 2, Bart handed off to Jimmy Taylor. The hole was open, but Jimmy never reached it. He stumbled on the Eagle 5 and was hauled to the ground. The Packers had missed a golden opportunity.

Not long after, the Packers were handed another chance. Green Bay linebacker Bill Forester recovered a Philadelphia fumble on the Eagle 22-yard line. This time Bart went to the air but his passes were off target. The Pack had to settle for a field goal.

Still another touchdown opportunity went by the boards late in the second quarter. Deep in Eagle territory, Bart handed off to Paul Hornung on an option play. Hornung had Boyd Dowler wide open, but instead of throwing a bullet, Hornung tried to steer the ball. It wobbled and was short and was easily batted down. Again the Packers settled for a field goal, making the score 6–0.

The Eagles got going in the second quarter. Van Brocklin connected with Tommy McDonald for a touchdown, the play covering 35 yards. Later in the period Bobby Walston booted a 15-yard field goal. Now the Eagles led, 10–6.

Three minutes remained in the half. Bart brought the Packers downfield to within the shadow of the Eagles' goal. With less than a minute left, the Packers lined up without a huddle to try a field goal. The confusion that resulted looked like a scene from a Jerry Lewis movie. Two Eagles had lined up on the Packer side of the ball. Then a fight broke out. An official whistled the play to a halt.

Now only five seconds remained. The ball was snapped. Bart held. Hornung, hurrying, booted. The ball went wide to the left.

Bart's eyes were on his shoe tops as he ran for the locker room. His team was four points behind, but they might easily have been leading by two or three touchdowns. But Bart was determined not to let the team's bad fortune get him down.

"We've been moving the ball well," he thought. "We'll win this thing yet."

Neither team scored in the third period since the defensive units excelled. As the final period of play began, Philadelphia still clung to a 10–6 lead.

Early in the fourth quarter, the Packers began to click. On the Eagle 34, Bart handed to Tom Moore for 12 yards and to Taylor for 6 more. Then Moore got 8 yards more and Taylor 3.

Bart then called Max McGee on a slant pattern. It worked to perfection. Touchdown! The Packers led, 13–10. Thirteen minutes remained.

Philadelphia roared back. Ted Dean took the kickoff and streaked 58 yards to the Packer 39. As the Philadelphia fans screamed encouragement, Van Brocklin steered his runners through the tiring Green Bay defenders. Ted Dean scored the touchdown from 5 yards out, and Walston converted.

Nine minutes were left when the Packers got the ball. Immediately Starr got the team rolling. He hit Max McGee for a 12-yard gain, but Max was jarred loose from the ball, and Bednarik recovered for the Eagles on the Philadelphia 48.

Van Brocklin called running plays in an attempt to run out the clock. Finally he was forced to punt. Again the Eagle defense stopped the Pack. When Green Bay got the ball back again, there were sixty-five seconds left and 65 yards to go. Bart Starr was about to face the biggest test of his career!

"We can still win this!" Bart told the team in the huddle. Every man knew they needed a touchdown. A field goal would leave them one point short.

Bart called a short pass to Taylor. It was good for 5 yards. Then he hit Tom Moore for 4. On the next play, Bart sent Jimmy Taylor around left end. Taylor almost broke free, and the crowd gasped. As it was, Jimmy made 9 yards and a first down.

Bart glanced at the black minute hand as it swept toward zero. "No more running plays," he thought. 'It's got to be all in the air from now on."

Bart took the snap from center and drifted back. The protection held. Standing at midfield, Bart spotted Gary Knafelc open near the Philadelphia 30-yard line.

He let go. Gary reached up and gathered in the ball and was tackled immediately. It was first down, and now the end zone was within reach.

There was time for two more passes, maybe three. Not a single time-out remained. The team scrambled to save precious seconds.

Bart missed on a pass to Dowler. The clock stopped. A pass to Knafelc got 8 yards. It was third down on the Eagle 22. The clock was moving again.

There wasn't enough time for a huddle. The ball was snapped, and Bart scrambled back. He looked for McGee, saw that he was covered, then targeted on Taylor at the Philadelphia 10.

He fired. Taylor, streaking toward the end zone, made the grab, then put his head down and exploded toward the goal. The Eagle defensemen lunged for him. Dan Burroughs missed. Maxie Baughan slowed him down. Then Bednarik roared in, smashing Taylor to the ground.

The gun went off. The Packers had come close, but close doesn't count. The record book lists the Philadelphia Eagles as the 1960 champions of the National Football League.

The Packer locker room was as quiet as a tomb. "We should have made more of our early chances," said Lombardi. "Van Brocklin is a great quarterback. We have no excuses. They outscored us. That's all that matters."

Bart slumped on the bench in front of his locker. His green shirt was torn, and his gold pants were streaked with mud. A jagged cut ran across the bridge of his nose. Every bone in his body seemed to ache.

"Nice game, Bart," someone said. Starr had completed twenty-one passes out of thirty-five, including the touchdown throw to McGee. Not one of his tosses had been intercepted.

Bart acknowledged the compliment with a half-hearted shrug. "Nice game?" he said. "What was so nice about it? We lost, didn't we?"

He wiped the back of his hand across the slash on his nose. His eyes narrowed. "I'm going to remember this day for a long, long time," he said. "But I'll tell you one thing. Nothing like this is going to happen to the Packers again, not while I'm quarterback. The next time we get a chance to go all the way, we're not going to blow it. I promise you that."

7

Coach

BART STARR COULD NOW look back upon five years as a professional quarterback. At this stage in his career, he was a very long way from enjoying the superstar status he holds today.

"Competent" and "efficient"—those were the words often used to describe him.

Starr was not nearly as well known as some of the other quarterbacks in the league. One reason for this was the Lombardi-style offense of the period, which emphasized the run much more than the pass. Thus, the headlines usually went to the versatile Paul Hornung, who could not only run, but pass, kick, and catch passes. In 1960, the Notre Dame "Goldilocks" established himself as the greatest of all one-season point makers, scoring 176 points. The newspapers were also quick to salute fullback Jimmy Taylor, who could churn his way through defensive backs with startling power and fury.

Another and not unimportant reason for Bart's lack of renown at this time was his own modesty. Bart Starr did not care to talk about the accomplishments of Bart Starr.

He preferred to talk about his blockers. A typical postgame comment from Bart would go, "Anybody could have completed those passes with the protection I got." Or he would laud his receivers—Boyd Dowler, Max McGee, and Ron Kramer.

Bart, during this period, was often damned with faint praise. Occasionally there was stern criticism.

"It's Starr's job not to foul things up," said one critic. "He just keeps the ball on the ground, passes enough to keep the defense honest, eats up the clock, and lets the defense demolish the opposition.

"And he's only a so-so passer. Sure, he completes a lot of passes, but that's only because the defenses have to concentrate on stopping the running game."

Don Schiffer, one of the country's leading sports prognosticators of the day, picked the Packers to finish second to the 49ers in the Western Conference in 1961. Schiffer had warm praise for the Green Bay running game, but he saw small chinks in the team's defense. And he had this to say about Bart: "Bart Starr has won permanent possession of quarterback, and here is where Green Bay may fall off a hair in quality. He has a tendency to ask his runners to carry too much of the load, and this does not add up to the most balanced of attacks, particularly if Taylor or Hornung crop up with injury because of an overload of assignments."

Bart Starr has won permanent possession of quarterback, and here is where Green Bay may fall off a hair in quality.

Harsh criticism.

What about Coach Lombardi? How did the coach feel about his quarterback? Did he agree with the press? Nobody knew for certain. There were only rumors.

One reporter wrote that Lombardi was upset with Starr, that Bart had missed seeing Max McGee in the end zone on a crucial play, and the slipup had cost the Pack the 1960 championship game. This reporter said that Lombardi believed the team needed more intelligence, more craftiness at quarterback. Lombardi was supposed to be casting covetous eyes toward Don Meredith of the Dallas Cowboys.

Bart read the stories. They did nothing to bolster his confidence.

How *did* Lombardi feel?

Late in March, 1961, Lombardi suddenly made his feelings known. He did it by trading away Lamar McHan. With this gesture, he was saying to Starr, "You're it. You're No. 1 in Green Bay. We're going all the way with you."

When the training season began, Bart's attitude was much different. "The trade really gave me the confidence I needed," Bart said.

"It does a lot for a person," Starr told *Sport* magazine later in his career, "to know that someone has the confidence to gamble on you. Believe me, that year I had nothing on my mind except justifying Lombardi's decision to trade Lamar away."

Lombardi had come to have high regard for Bart's skills. He respected Bart for his intelligence and desire. In his book *Run to Daylight!* Lombardi declared, "At our quarterback meetings, even though he was not first string, Starr could repeat almost verbatim everything we had discussed the previous three days . . . ." Bart's dedication was another thing that impressed the coach. He noted that Starr was always borrowing game films to take home and study.

He praised Starr for his "analytic mind, retentive memory, and inner toughness . . . . " He is "great," Lombardi said, at picking apart defenses and adjusting.

He lauded Bart for his ability to kill the opposition with short passes—"those singles and doubles," Lombardi called them—but he fretted because Bart "doesn't throw those home runs often enough." Said Lombardi, "If I could just get him to be a little more daring, he'd be everything."

The trading of Lamar McHan was only one part of Lombardi's grand design to make Bart Starr "everything," to turn a silent, sometimes sulky young man into a poised and confident leader.

Was Lombardi successful? Bart himself is the best authority for the answer to this. Once, after he had been with the team for more than a decade, Bart looked back upon his first season under the leadership of Lombardi. "When Lombardi started working with me, I knew that I knew nothing," said Bart. "You can't imagine how totally inept I was. He showed me every-thing—how to scout defenses, where to look, where to go with the ball.

"Lombardi's personality rubs off on you," Bart told John Davaney. "He is a demanding, driving person who will not settle for second best. When you are around him long enough, you begin to think like him. You even begin to act like him.

"You become demanding and driving. You will not settle for second best.

"I am a totally different person for having worked with Coach Lombardi."

Vince Lombardi was born in New York City on June 11, 1913, the son of an Italian immigrant, a butcher. His father was a strict disciplinarian. "He had an abiding respect for mental toughness," Lombardi has often said.

Young Vince made his high school team as a full-back and played well enough to win a scholarship to Fordham University. There he was switched to guard and became a member of one of the most famous football lines of all time, Fordham's vaunted "Seven Blocks of Granite."

Jim Crowley, the left halfback on Notre Dame's "Four Horsemen" backfield in 1924, was the Fordham coach at the time, and it was from Crowley that Lombardi learned about football's "fourth dimen-sion." The first three dimensions, says Lombardi, are material, coaching, and the schedule. The fourth is "selfless teamwork and collective pride." These qualities, Lombardi believes, lead to positive thinking and help make victory become a habit.

After he graduated from Fordham in 1937, Lombardi attended law school for two years. He did his first coaching—basketball and baseball as well as football—at St. Cecilia's High School in Englewood, New Jersey. Later he returned to Fordham as an assistant football coach. Then Colonel Earl H. "Red" Blaik hired Lombardi to coach the offensive line at West Point. Lombardi left Army in 1954 to join the New York Giants as offensive coach under Jim Lee Howell. In his five years with the Giants, the team won the Eastern Division title three times and the NFL championship once. Then came the Packers.

From his first day with the Packers, Lombardi toiled to bring the team into top-notch physical condition. "Nobody in less than prime condition can play football well very long," he said. In order to achieve the proper level of condition, a player must be willing to be driven beyond limits he believes possible to endure, Lombardi stated. Occasionally the coach was criticized for the ruggedness of his conditioning program. His defense was that it would be a greater form of brutality to send an underconditioned team into a football game.

Lombardi does not hesitate to admit that pro football is a violent game, but it is violence as distinct from brutality. "Brutality," he states, "defeats itself." It is one of Lombardi's guiding principles that "the dirty player not only breaks the rules but hurts the team and himself." Lombardi demands that the game be played cleanly.

It was not enough, however, to be merely physically tough under Lombardi. That was only half of it. He stressed mental toughness, too.

When asked to define mental toughness, Lombardi would reply, "It's a state of mind. You've got to accept making mistakes without letting them beat you."

Lombardi, like other coaches in the league, realized that mistakes were inevitable. But he never let one go by unchallenged, even on the practice field. He rebuked both rookies and veteran players whenever he felt a blunder had been committed. The amount of criticism he meted out depended on the individual.

A tongue-lashing from Vince Lombardi could be a memorable experience. Once, defensive tackle Henry Jordan jokingly remarked, "Coach treats us all the same—just like dogs."

But it was Lombardi's theory that a player who could take his censure after making a mistake would be far less likely to lose his poise after making a mistake before 50,000 people.

Mental toughness.

That is the principal quality that Bart Starr developed under Vince Lombardi.

The first time that Lombardi saw Starr throw a football was in the fall of 1959 in a team scrimmage. Bart dropped back, saw that his receivers were covered, but threw anyway, hoping the man he had tar-

geted on would leap high and make the grab. The pass
was batted down.

When Bart came off the field, Lombardi was waiting. And he was boiling. "One more like that," Lombardi barked, "and you're through. There aren't going
to be any pass-and-pray quarterbacks on this club."

Bart took Lombardi's tongue-lashings stoically. He
did not answer back. But they hurt.

"I don't like to get chewed out," Bart once said. "No
one does. It hurts your pride. It hurts you a little inside,
and I guess it's human nature when anyone gets on
you, no matter how right he is, to rebel a little." But
Bart gritted his teeth, sucked in his belly, and kept the
rebellion bottled up inside.

Lombardi also taught Bart not to brood over errors.
"This had been my weakness for years," Bart says.

How thoroughly Bart soaked up Lombardi's mental
toughness doctrine is revealed by this incident. It took
place one season not too long after Lombardi had
taken over the coaching reins.

It was a season in which the Bears and the Colts
were rated as the Packers' toughest rivals for the
Western Conference championship. On opening day
Green Bay had whipped the Bears, while the Colts
were losing. The next week the Packers faced the
Colts. Were Baltimore to lose, their record would be
0–2, and they would be about out of it.

It was a fierce game. Both teams scored three touchdowns, but the Packers missed one of their extra-point
attempts. They trailed by that one point as the game

was drawing to a close. About a minute remained. Green Bay had the ball. The Packers called a time-out, and Bart went to the bench to talk to Lombardi.

The coach had a play ready. He told Bart to use a flood pattern left and to throw to Ron Kramer on the right. If it worked, it would get the team in field-goal range. But in the huddle Starr let Max McGee talk him into a different pattern, one that had McGee as the primary receiver and Tom Moore as the secondary man.

The ball was snapped. Bart faked a hand-off to Jim Taylor, then drifted back. As he cocked his arm, he saw McGee just making his fake.

Bart then looked for Moore but he couldn't spot him. Maybe he had been dropped. Maybe he was shielded from Starr's view by linemen. Bart looked back to McGee. His heart sank. McGee was covered.

Starr knew then that he'd blown it. He threw in McGee's direction, but high, intending the ball to go over Max's head and out of bounds. But just as Bart unloaded, a Colt lineman broke through and hit his arm. The ball wobbled crazily, then fluttered toward the ground like a sick bird. Don Shinnick, the Colts' right linebacker, made an easy interception. A few seconds later the game ended. Starr had really blown it!

In the locker room, Lombardi lashed out at Bart in front of the team. Perhaps the play Lombardi wanted would not have worked any better, but the coach maintained it would have. Bart agreed with him. That night when Bart got home, he wept.

The Packers didn't win the championship that year. Baltimore did. Bart has admitted that it was he who might have cost the Packers the title.

But what is important is that Bart didn't let the incident destroy him. If it had taken place a year or two before, it might have. But he didn't dwell upon it. He blotted the game out of his mind. He dedicated himself to not letting it happen again. That was being mentally tough.

When the great Knute Rockne coached Notre Dame in the late 1920's and early 1930's, the quarterback was his vicar on the field. Rockne wanted his quarterback to be respected, and the man was never a target for Rockne's occasional bursts of sarcasm.

The Lombardi-Starr relationship was somewhat the same. "I'm Coach Lombardi's representative on the field," Bart once said. "I'm doing what he would be doing if he were quarterback. If he's happy with the way I'm doing my job, I don't care how anyone else reacts.

"If people regard me as a push-button quarterback, I take it as a compliment. It means that I've absorbed and am able to apply things Coach has taught me over the years."

Lombardi could see Starr's confidence build. Once the learning stage was passed, he noticed that Bart would argue a point if he felt the coach was in error.

And there was other evidence. One day after Lombardi had been with Green Bay for about two years, Bart brought his contract into Lombardi's office and placed it on the coach's desk.

Lombardi examined the last page. The contract was unsigned.

"A couple of years ago, I'd have signed anything you gave me," Bart said. "But you've taught me to be more aggressive and self-assertive." And then he stated the salary he wanted.

Telling of the incident in *Run to Daylight!*, Lombardi quoted himself as saying, "So that's it. Like Frankenstein, I've created a monster."

On the banquet circuit, Bart often makes light of Lombardi's legendary cussedness. This is one story he tells: "A lot of people ask me how I happened to become the quarterback for the Green Bay Packers. Well, when Vince Lombardi took over the team, he built a big brick wall at one end of the practice field, and he had the players run toward it. The ones who smacked into it and fell backward he made defensive linemen. The ones who smacked into it and fell on their bellies became offensive linemen. The ones who ran through it became fullbacks. And the ones who ran up to the wall and then walked around it became quarterbacks."

While it was sometimes the subject of their humor, it is no secret that Starr and the other players did regard Lombardi with a certain awe. They always addressed him as Coach. Not as *the* coach, but simply as Coach, as in the sentence "Coach wants to see you."

Paul Hornung once broke up his teammates with a story that reflected the reverence with which the players regarded Lombardi. The Packers had returned to

Green Bay at 2 A.M. after beating the Rams in Los Angeles. A crowd of well-wishers greeted the team at the airport, this in spite of the near-zero temperature.

Lombardi was delayed for about an hour talking to the press and fans and signing autographs. By the time he arrived home, the coach was chilled to the bone.

When Lombardi finally climbed into bed, his wife, Marie, broke into shivers. "God," she exclaimed, "your feet are like ice."

Lombardi, according to Hornung, calmly replied, "In bed, dear, you may call me Vincent."

8

"The Greatest Team"

THE PACKERS HAD JUST MISSED winning the championship in 1960. Coming close was no fun. They were in a vengeful mood as the season of 1961 approached.

They were now a tough, talented team, manned by personnel whose names were soon to become familiar to every football fan. The offensive line was bulwarked by center Jim Ringo and guards Fuzzy Thurston and Jerry Kramer. Forrest Gregg and Bob Skoronski were the tackles.

Bart's receivers were developing into the finest in football. For the 1961 season, Lombardi moved Ron Kramer into the starting lineup as a tight end. Kramer had jet speed getting started and was just a blur when slanting out to grab a pass, or he could block out the middle linebacker with all the authority of a pulling guard. Max McGee was already as cool and accomplished as any receiver around. Boyd Dowler was beginning to come into his own as a flanker. Soon he would be All-Pro.

The team played five preseason games and won them all. Bart made few mistakes.

Then the team stumbled, losing the opening game of the league season to Detroit. Several times the blocking broke down, and Bart spent a good part of the afternoon looking at the sky.

But the team rebounded, beating San Francisco and Chicago in quick succession. Bart remembers the game against the Bears. On one play big Bill George, the Bears' 6-foot 3-inch, 235-pound linebacker, came careening in, and his elbow caught Bart square in the face. The blow split Bart's lip, and blood flowed.

Bart took a deep breath and gritted his teeth, then wiped the back of his hand across his mouth. On the very next play he rifled a touchdown pass to Boyd Dowler.

San Francisco fell before the Packer onslaught the next week, and then the Cleveland Browns.

Bart had a phenomenal day against the Browns. He hit on fifteen out of seventeen passes for 272 yards. It could have been even more fantastic. "One of the two passes that Bart failed to complete," Paul Hornung recalls, "I dropped."

The final score saw the Packers on top, 49–14. In the locker room after, Lombardi said it was the best game the team had ever played.

The Packers then played two successive games against the Vikings and won both of them.

Their winning streak had now reached six games. They were beginning to see a championship in their future.

But the next week the Packers' dreams were shattered by the Baltimore Colts, a team that they had whipped earlier in the season. Bart had a trying day and had to scurry out of the pocket several times. He completed only seven passes out of eighteen attempts. Meanwhile, Johnny Unitas could not do anything wrong. He hit on twenty-two passes out of thirty-six, four for touchdowns. Baltimore won, 45–21.

The Packers now owned a 6–2 record, which was good enough to earn them first place in the Western Conference standings. But Chicago, at 5–3, was right behind.

The following Sunday the two teams came face-to-face. It was a game the Packers had to win. They rolled to a 28–7 lead in the first half, then hung on desperately as Chicago rallied. The Packers' margin of victory was only three points, 31–28.

The next week the Packers downed the Rams, and they followed that victory by avenging their opening game loss to the Detroit Lions.

The Packers now boasted a 9–2 record. Three games remained on the schedule. To clinch the Western championship, Green Bay had to win only one of those games.

The New York Giants came to town, confident and brash. Many fans looked on the game as a possible preview of the title contest of the champions in the West and East.

The Giants owned two of the game's most cunning quarterbacks in Y. A. Tittle and Charlie Conerly. The latter was playing his last season of a long and much-honored career.

The Giants' defense, rated as the best in the NFL the season before, was staffed by well-seasoned specialists. Sam Huff, their All-Pro middle linebacker, was one of the league's fiercest defensemen, and one of the sharpest experts in diagnosing plays. Andy Robustelli and Jim Katcavage held down the ends, and Dick Modzelewski and Rosey Grier the tackles.

The teams battled grimly for three quarters. New York held a 17–13 lead.

Then the Giants' running game began to click, and it seemed they were going to increase their lead. But something happened.

Early in the fourth quarter, New York had the ball on their own 8-yard line. Tittle handed off to Alex Webster, who suddenly broke into the clear and headed downfield. He was nearing Green Bay territory when Henry Jordan slammed into him, spinning Webster around. As he, Webster, was turning, Packer defensive back Jesse Whittenton met him head on. But instead of spilling Webster, Whittenton slid a hand inside Webster's enfolded arms and snatched the ball away. Whittenton did not get much yardage because Webster tackled him right away, but in that instant the momentum of the attack shifted from the Giants to the Packers.

When Bart led the offensive team out onto the field, he could feel the confidence building. It took him only four plays to engineer a touchdown. He handed off to Jimmy Taylor who carried it in. Now the Packers were ahead, 20–17, and that was the score at the final gun.

It was a bitter defeat for the New Yorkers. They were convinced they should have won. "Don't worry, fellas," said Y. A. Tittle in the Giant dressing room. "We'll play 'em again."

Tittle proved prophetic. About a month later on an icy cold December day, the two teams met, and this time the championship of the National Football League was at stake.

Green Bay was the site of duel, and the town went slightly mad. Any football game involving the Packers is enough to set Green Bay aflutter, but this was to be the first title game in the city's history, and the citizens bubbled with hysteria.

Store owners hung out signs that proclaimed Green Bay's newest nickname—Titletown, U.S.A. When the Giants arrived in Green Bay and saw the signs, one member of the team suggested the name needed an extra T—so it would read Tittletown, in honor of the New Yorkers' quarterback.

The temperature never got as "high" as freezing on the day of the game. The Packers took the bitter cold pretty much in stride, but it disturbed the Giants. During the pregame warm-ups, they experimented with sneakers on the frozen field, then switched back to cleated shoes for the game. The New York defensemen wore gloves.

Fifteen minutes before the kickoff, the Packers were back in their locker room for Lombardi's final words.

Bart sat quietly in the crowded room, his helmet on his lap. The biggest game of his life was about to begin. He could feel the butterflies.

"I know you can win," Lombardi began. "You should have won the championship last year, and you know it. So let's not make any mistakes. This game means a lot to you—in money and prestige."

Lombardi's voice was louder now, earnest and commanding. "Be alert! Let's go get 'em!"

Let's go get 'em!

The words were ringing in Bart's brain as he trotted down the ramp and onto the field. Slightly more than 39,000 people were in the stands, and they stood and cheered wildly when the team came out.

The Packers kicked off, but the Giants could not move the ball and had to punt. Now it was Green Bay's turn.

Bart's heart was pounding as he raced out onto the field. He knew exactly what to do. There were to be no trick plays, no offbeat formations. The Packers were going to play old-fashioned, hard-nosed football.

The team broke from the huddle, and when Bart came up to the ball, he saw at once that New York had thrown up a surprise defense—a five-man front line. They had always before played a traditional 4-3 defense.

Bart handed off to Paul Hornung, who got 6 yards. But the next two plays were stopped cold, and now the Packers had to punt back.

The Giants took over on their own 31-yard line and moved to midfield. From there they had to kick again.

Now Bart went to work, calling plays with deadly precision. In the previous game against the Giants, the Packers had run their plays to the right side. This time Bart went to the left.

He knew how to cope with the five-man line. On the snap, he took the ball and handed to Hornung. Kramer blocked in on the tackle, and Ringo, Gregg, and Skoronski pulled to lead the way, wiping out the Giant linemen. The first time Bart called the play Hornung got 4 yards.

Then Bart passed, hitting Hornung for 26 yards. Now the ball was at midfield, and Bart had breathing room.

He handed off to Hornung for 5 yards, then to Taylor, and then to Taylor again. He went to Taylor once more, then faked to Taylor and gave the ball to Hornung. The Packers were deep in Giant territory now. Moments later the New Yorkers were hit with a pass interference penalty that gave the Packers a first down on the Giant 7-yard line.

Seven yards to go for a touchdown. The big New York line, the most ferocious in pro football, dug in.

When the Packers came up to the ball, Bart surveyed the Giant defense and saw immediately that Sam Huff had stationed himself slightly to the right of center. His idea was to shut off Jim Taylor's off-tackle slant to the right—the play that had hurt New York so badly in the first game.

Bart's face was a mask as he called the signals, not even the twitch of an eye indicating that he had "read" what Huff was doing. "Thirty-seven, sixty-two," Bart's voice rang out. "Hut! . . . Hut!" The ball snapped back and Bart faked to Taylor. The New York line rose up to meet him, and the loud crack of shell plastic meeting shell plastic filled the air.

But Bart handed to Hornung. "Five! . . . Five!" came the desperate cry of a Giant lineman, calling out Hornung's number to his teammates. But the warning came too late. Hornung had a clear alley all the way to the end zone.

Hornung then kicked the extra point, and the Packers were ahead, 7–0.

After receiving the kickoff, the Giants got into trouble again. Tittle, trying a pass, saw Ray Nitschke intercept. For a moment it seemed that Nitschke might score, but Giant tacklers brought him down on the New York 34.

Bart tried two passes, and both went incomplete. It was third down and 10; the pressure was on. Again Bart drifted back, the ball at his ear. This time his pass was perfect, and the Packers had a first down on the New York 18-yard line.

Bart sent Taylor into the line twice, but he got only 5 yards. Bart was faced with another tough third-down call. He took the snap and stepped back coolly, then arched the ball to Boyd Dowler in the end zone. Hornung's kick made it 14–0.

The Packer defense had Tittle under constant pressure. Often he had to scurry about with the Green Bay linemen in pursuit, finally throwing in desperation. In one such situation he was intercepted again, this time by Henry Gremminger, who was brought down on the New York 36-yard line.

Hornung and Taylor then took turns punishing the New York line. In seven plays they moved the ball to the Giant 14. It was second down.

The Packers huddled. "Flood right," Bart whispered. It was a perfect call.

As the ball slapped into Bart's hands, a swarm of receivers—three of them—hooked and slanted to the right side. The Giant defense moved to cover.

Meanwhile, on the left side, big Ron Kramer had thrown a savage block at the New York linebacker on that side. The linebacker figured Kramer couldn't possibly be going out for a pass. He fought off the block, then released Kramer. The middle was clear because Huff had gone to the right where Bart had sent the receivers.

But Kramer *was* a receiver. When Bart fired to him, Kramer was streaking through the area that Huff had vacated. He made the catch, then bolted into the end zone.

The Packer fans, wrapped in blankets and robes, some with ear muffs, some with face masks, and all with gloves or mittens, cheered in happy disbelief.

The Giants launched a mild threat after the kickoff, driving to the Green Bay 6-yard line. But there the Packer line stopped the Giants cold.

With time in the first half running out, Bart brought his team downfield once more. There were only a few seconds left on the clock when Hornung booted a field goal to put the Packers ahead, 24–0.

The second half brought more of the same.

Early in the third period, Bart called another "flood right," but this he varied in play a bit. The Green Bay receivers broke to the right side, just as they had the first time. And the Giant defense cleared out to cover.

Ron Kramer, after delivering his block, slipped into the middle, but the Giants had Joe Morrison covering him. Bart had expected this. He faked to Kramer, who paused for just an instant, then zipped away from Morrison to the outside and into the end zone. Bart hit him with a perfect pitch.

The Packers now led, 31–0. In the final period Hornung kicked another field goal to make the score 34–0. That's how it stood when the final gun sounded.

The players yelled loudly and clapped one another on the back as they filed into the dressing room. Once they were inside, Lombardi barred the door to reporters. He held up his hands, and the clamor ceased. The players turned to listen to their coach.

It was an emotional moment for Lombardi. His hand kept going to his glasses.

"Today," he said in a raspy voice, "you were the greatest team in the history of the National Football League."

Then the doors were opened, and the reporters and television people flooded in. Lombardi was immediately surrounded.

"Starr performed like a champion," the coach declared. "He called the plays and made the offensive changes that were needed. He knew exactly what I wanted. He followed our ready sheet for the game perfectly. We won because we made very, very few mistakes."

Another cluster of reporters encircled Paul Hornung. His nineteen points were a new play-off game scoring record, and he was named the game's Most Valuable Player.

Ron Kramer, who had grabbed two touchdown passes, was another center of attention. And reporters also crowded about Willie Davis, a star on defense.

Bart Starr? Bart sat on a bench before his locker stall, an almost forgotten figure in the locker room melee. Only a small sprinkling of reporters sought him out.

"How does it feel," one asked, "to be the youngster who outsmarted Y. A. Tittle?"

Bart's brow furrowed. "I wouldn't exactly put it that way," Bart declared. "I didn't try to match wits with Y. A. We won as a team."

Bart and the Packers were to win many more championships in the years that followed, but there would never be another like this. This was the first. This was special.

The greatest team in the history of the National Football League—that's what Vince Lombardi had called the 1961 Packers. The fans of Green Bay were in wholehearted agreement with Lombardi's appraisal. Before the 1962 season was very old, just about everyone else was ready to agree with him, too.

The Packers opened the season by trimming the Vikings, 34–7. The next week they turned back the Cardinals, 17–0. They whipped the Bears, 49–10.

Then Detroit came into Green Bay. The Lion defensemen, with their stunting and blitzing tactics, made it a painful day for Bart. A field goal by Paul Hornung in the game's last minute saved the day. The final score was 9–6.

"This is the team we're going to have to beat out for the Western Conference championship," Bart said after the game, "and it's not going to be easy."

After Detroit, the Packers breezed by Minnesota. They then beat San Francisco, Baltimore, Chicago, and Philadelphia on successive weekends and all by big scores.

The Philadelphia game was a runaway, the Packers winning, 49–0. Green Bay was as perfect that day as any team can be. They piled up a fantastic 628 yards on total offense.

As the teams were leaving the field at half time, with the Green Bay rout already apparent, Philadelphia linebacker Chuck Bednarik walked up to Packer end coach Tom Fears. "Tom," Bednarik said, "when do you put in the scrubs?"

Fears shook his head. "Chuck," he answered, "this team doesn't have any scrubs."

Tough Baltimore went down the next week. That made it ten wins in a row for the Packers.

The greatest team in the history of the National Football League. Very few doubted it now.

Detroit was the next opponent. Following their early-in-the-season loss to the Packers, the Lions had dropped only one other game. But they realized that they now had to whip the Packers to stay in contention.

The game was played on Thanksgiving Day morning in Tiger Stadium. It was cruelly cold, and a bitter wind whipped the field.

On the Packers' first play from scrimmage, Detroit's Alex Karras and Roger Brown broke through the Green Bay defenses and smashed Bart to the ground. Karras was 6 feet 2 inches and weighed 245 pounds. Brown was even bigger. He stood 6 feet 2 inches and weighed 300. When they struck together, Bart felt like a building had fallen on him.

Karras and Brown did it again and again, much to the glee of the Detroit fans. Each time, Bart would pull himself to his feet, then stumble dazedly into the huddle to call another play.

Nothing seemed to go right. Once Brown hurled Bart to the ground in the end zone, costing the Packers two points. The Lions led, 7–0, at the end of the first quarter; they led 23–0 at the half.

In the second half, the Packers went out determined to halt the Lions' blitz. Bart had a play he thought would help—a quick pass to Ron Kramer, who was to hook into the area vacated by blitzing linebacker Wayne Walker. Bart knew if he could complete the pass, the Lions would become much more wary of rushing in on him.

The ball was on the Green Bay 42-yard line when Bart called the play. He scampered back to pass, then looked for Kramer. What he saw made Bart's heart sink. Walker wasn't going to blitz; he had dropped off and was covering Kramer like a blanket.

Bart looked to his No. 2 receiver. He was covered, too. Nobody was open.

Bart could see his pass protection beginning to break down. Powerful arms grabbed him about the chest and flung him to the frozen ground.

When Bart walked to the huddle, he was shaking his head sadly. "It's just one of those games," he was thinking. Soon after, the Lions were on their way to another touchdown. They won with ease, 26–14.

But the Packers bounced back like the champions they were. They bowled over the Rams the next week, 41–10, with Bart passing for two touchdowns. But Detroit won, too, to remain in the running.

The following Sunday the Packers played in Kezar Stadium in San Francisco. The 49ers led at the half, 21–10. That was not the worst. The Lions had already won their game, and the Packers knew it.

In the Green Bay dressing room, Lombardi called for silence. "If we lose this game," he bellowed, "it looks like we'll have a play-off on our hands. Well, we don't want any play-off.

"You defensive men, go out there and hit. You fellows on offense, put some points on the board."

Bart went out for the second half with his mind made up to follow Lombardi's instructions—to put some points on the board. On the first play of the second half, he threw to Taylor for a first down. He fired again and hit. Then he called the Packers' power sweep, handing to Hornung who turned the end and careened into the end zone. That made the score 21–17, San Francisco.

In the fourth quarter, Bart riddled the 49ers' defense with short passes, blending his aerial attack with handoffs to Taylor and Hornung. The Packers scored two more touchdowns, burying San Francisco, 31–21.

The next week, the final week of the season, the Packers downed the Rams to clinch their third consecutive Western Conference championship.

Before the 1962 season opened, Bart had set a personal goal for himself—to cut down on his interceptions. In 1961 he had seen 16 of his 295 passes intercepted, a fine record. But Bart wanted to improve it. "It kills you when you give up the ball on interceptions," he said. "If you don't have the ball in this game, you don't score."

Bart achieved his goal. In 1962, he attempted about the same number of passes as in 1961—285. But his number of interceptions dropped to 9. Bart took this as a meaningful personal victory.

The 1962 National League title game was a rematch between the Packers and the Giants. It was played in New York City, but in typical Green Bay weather. The temperature at game time was 17 degrees. Worse, strong and icy winds swirled about Yankee Stadium throughout the afternoon, whipping the players relentlessly.

The Giants were itching for revenge. Some of their fans displayed banners that carried the words "Remember 1961!"

The game was a brawl, trench warfare, a desperate slugging match.

The fierce cold and raging wind hampered the Giants' air attack. There were times that Y. A. Tittle's frozen-fingered receivers simply could not get their hands to grasp the ball. But the same wind lashed the Packers. Bart reacted by concentrating on the running game.

Green Bay scored first. Late in the first quarter, using straight-ahead running plays and power sweeps, Bart brought the Packers 61 yards in ten plays. The attack ground to a halt on the New Yorkers' 19-yard line. Jerry Kramer, filling in for Paul Hornung, whose kicking leg had been injured, booted a field goal, and Green Bay led, 3–0.

The next time the Packers scored by combining roughneck football with daring and finesse.

In the second quarter, Tittle sent a crisp pass to Phil King. Linebacker Dan Currie was waiting, and he cannoned into King just as the Giant receiver got his hands on the ball. Ray Nitschke pounced on the fumble that resulted.

So much for the roughhousing. The boldness that followed was Bart's doing.

With the ball on the New York 28-yard line, Bart called a pass—despite the almost gale-force wind. He was figuring the element of surprise would make the move a worthwhile gamble.

Bart took the snap, turned, and quickly handed to Hornung. The "Golden Boy" tucked the ball to his belly and roared toward the surging Giant line, then suddenly he stopped and pitched to Boyd Dowler. The play got 21 yards.

With first down on the Giant 7, Bart gave the ball to Jimmy Taylor, and the strong-legged fullback churned his way into the end zone. Jerry Kramer added the extra point, and Green Bay led, 10–0.

"I thought that play might work," Starr was to say after. "We had Taylor going to the right side, and I think we caught [Sam] Huff thinking we were going left. Jimmy had a clear alley to the end zone."

The first half ended soon after Taylor's touchdown.

The Giants came out for the third quarter doubly determined to spring back. Three times the Packers got their hands on the ball, and three times the scrappy Giant defenders forced them to punt.

On the third kick, Max McGee took the snap while standing on the Green Bay 3-yard line. He held the ball in front of his body, then swung his right leg through. In fired the Giants' Erich Barnes, his hands reaching for the sky, and he punched the ball into the end zone. Jim Collier fell on it for the Giants. When Don Chandler added the extra point, the Packers' lead was down to three points, 10–7.

The half-frozen New York fans forgot the cold and screamed in delight.

Green Bay received the kickoff, but again Starr could not move the team. McGee punted—this time successfully; very successfully, in fact. The Giants' Sam Horner, poised to catch the ball, let it slip through his benumbed fingers. Right there to pounce on it was Ray Nitschke.

This time Bart led the Pack to the Giants' 29. Kramer came in and booted another field goal, lifting Green Bay's lead to six points, 13–7.

Throughout the rest of the Arcticlike afternoon, the Giants kept up a manful struggle to penetrate the Packers' end zone, but there were to be no more touchdowns. Whenever the Packers got the ball, Bart played cute, ball-control football, sending his bruised and bloodied backs hurtling into the Giant line. Late in the fourth period, Kramer booted another field goal, the last three points of the game.

The Packers were champions of the National Football League for the second consecutive year.

It was a distinctly different type of victory from the year before. In that one, the Packers had approached perfection. Their execution had been slick, without a flaw. But this time they had gone into the pit, scrambling and brawling in the refrigerator called Yankee Stadium.

"Did the cold weather bother you?" a reporter asked Bart after the game.

Bart managed a smile. "You know what Coach says," he answered.

"You're only cold when you lose."

9

"Back Where We Belong"

BART NEEDED NO REMINDER, but there it was— Paul Hornung's jersey. Someone had thumbtacked it to the door of the equipment locker in the Green Bay dressing room. The big No. 5 stood out like a signal light. Above the jersey, the person had nailed the nameplate from Hornung's locker stall.

Hornung would have no need for his jersey or any other piece of equipment during the season of 1963. He had been suspended by the commissioner of the National Football League, Pete Rozelle.

The reason? Paul had bet on NFL games. He had never bet on or against the Packers, never on any game in which he played. But every pro player's contract makes it clear that betting is about as acceptable as fielding a fifteen-man team.

Bart was one of the first to come to Hornung's defense. "People say that Paul is a wild-living guy," Bart declared, "but he's not. He's a real fine person. I ought to know. I've had the locker next to him for the last six years.

"Now people are going to find out just how fine a person Paul is. He made a mistake. He said he was sorry. He will come back to be an even greater football player."

Bart admitted that the team would miss Hornung's skills as a runner, kicker, and passer, plus his leadership ability.

"My son, Bart, Jr., will miss him, too," Bart noted. "He idolized Paul. He tells everybody that Paul is his favorite Packer."

Lombardi had speedy Tom Moore ready as Hornung's replacement, and two splendid understudies in Elijah Pitts and Earl Gros.

The season got off to a sorry start for Bart. The Packers faced the Bears. Chicago had developed an aggressive pass defense. It was manned by four speedsters—Bennie McRae, Dave Whitsell, Rich Petitbon, and Roosevelt Taylor. Each had dazzling speed and the reactions of a jungle cat.

In the opening game of the season, this quartet treated Bart in rude fashion. They batted many of his passes to the ground and intercepted four of them. Through all of the previous season, Bart had seen only nine of his passes intercepted.

The Packers' scoring production was limited to a single field goal, as the Bears won, 10–3.

Bart still remembers that game. There is one other that stands out in his memory during 1963.

The Packers faced the Cardinals in St. Louis. Play was in the third period. Green Bay had a comfortable lead.

Bart went back to pass but found his receivers covered. Then he noticed there were wide-open spaces dead ahead. He tucked the ball to his belly and started running. After a 15-yard pickup, St. Louis defenders began to close in. To avoid them Bart headed out of bounds.

But just before he reached the sideline, Cardinal defenseman Jimmy Hill thumped into Bart and slammed him to the ground. Bart landed on his right arm.

"It was like an auto accident," Bart was to say later. "I never knew what hit me."

Hopelessly dazed, Bart struggled to his feet. Max McGee rushed over and guided Bart to the Packer bench.

Bart's head quickly cleared, but every time he moved his right hand agonizing pain flashed through his wrist. It felt like the stab of a knife. Then the wrist began to swell. Lombardi ordered No. 2 quarterback John Roach into the game.

X rays were taken right after the game. Then Bart got the bad news. He had suffered a hairline fracture of a bone in his right hand.

Bart's arm was encased in a cast. He watched the next four games from the sidelines. John Roach did a first-rate job of filling in, leading the Pack to wins over Baltimore, Pittsburgh, and Minnesota.

The Packers were tied for first place with the Bears in the Western Conference standings when the two met in a showdown game at Wrigley Field. Roach encountered the same problem that Bart had had in the previous meeting of the teams—a remarkable pass defense. Five of Roach's passes were intercepted. On offense, the Bears played ball-control football, using fifty-five running plays. They won, 26–7.

Bart returned to the lineup the next week, and the Packers did not lose another game that season. But neither did the Bears.

The Conference championship was decided on the last weekend of the season. On Saturday, the Packers downed the 49ers, 21–17, with Bart throwing two touchdown passes. On Sunday, the Bears were to meet the Lions at Wrigley Field. The Western Conference standings—won, lost, and tied—looked like this before the game:

Chicago	10	1	2
Green Bay	11	2	1

The Packers realized that if the Bears lost, Green Bay would take the title. But if Chicago won, they would be the Conference champions.

Throughout the game, the Packer players stayed glued to their television sets. Detroit led at half-time, 7–3. The Packers were all smiles.

But in the third quarter, Chicago went ahead, 17–7. Detroit fought back and reduced the Bears' lead to a mere three points, 17–14.

In the closing minutes, the Lions had the ball, and quarterback Earl Morrall drifted back to pass. He threw—to Chicago's Dave Whitsell, who promptly turned the interception into a touchdown.

The Packers turned away from their TV sets. They were no longer league champions.

"The Bears deserved to win the conference title," was Bart's comment. "We had two games with them, and we lost them both."

Many people felt the Packers failed to win the championship because of the absence of Paul Hornung. Not Bart. "I don't think we missed Hornung that much," he declared. "Tom Moore had a great year for us and so did Elijah Pitts. I really don't think Paul's absence was the cause of our downfall. It was a case of losing twice to the same club. That's what beat us."

During the 1963 season, Bart established two Green Bay passing records. He completed 132 passes for a career record of 869, thereby eclipsing Tobin Rote's record of 826. Starr ran his yardage total to 11,730, to exceed Rote's mark of 11,535.

The Bears faced the Giants in the NFL championship game. Their pass defense was up to form, as they grabbed off five of Tittle's tosses. Chicago won, 14–10.

As a consolation prize, the Packers got to play the Cleveland Browns in the Play-off Bowl. Green Bay scored a resounding 40–23 victory. Yet the game did little to console the Packers. Indeed, nothing could have relieved their distress at being dethroned.

Green Bay's hopes were bright for 1964. Besides their gifted front liners and dependable reserves, the team could point to a highly promising group of rookies.

And there was more. Paul Hornung would be back, his suspension lifted.

But, as one observer was to note, "That suspension put some rust in Hornung's kicking leg."

The Packers lost three of their first three games by a total of only 5 points. Missed extra points caused the Packers to incur 1-point losses at the hands of the Colts and Vikings.

The Packer-Colt rematch was held in Baltimore, the sixth game of the season. The Packers, with a sad 3-2 record, knew they were going to beat Baltimore in order to stay in the title race.

With a minute and a half remaining in the game, the Packers led, 21–17. Then Hornung had his *fifth* field goal attempt blocked. Jerry Logan of the Colts picked up the loose ball. Shortly after, Baltimore scored the game-winning touchdown.

The Packers were in a state of shock when they filed into their dressing room. When Hornung got to his locker stall, he discovered that someone had put a fake pistol on the shelf. Jokingly, he put it to his head.

"Paul, Paul, don't shoot, for heaven's sake!" Bart called out in mock horror.

Jimmy Taylor was standing nearby. "Don't worry, Bart," he said, "He'll miss."

The Packers lost the following week to the Los Angeles Rams and a few weeks later were whipped by the San Francisco 49ers. Green Bay finished with an 8-5-1 record, which earned the club its second straight second-place finish.

Statistically, the Packers had a fine year. They had the league's best rushing attack. Bart was the NFL's top-ranked passer. He allowed only four interceptions.

Lombardi was not one to be impressed by statistics. "Some year," he grumbled. "We won everything but the championship."

The Packers did not intend to finish second again. "This year we're going to be number one," Lombardi told the players at the first team meeting of the new season. "If you don't think you're going to be number one, then I don't want you playing for me."

Lombardi traded away tight end Ron Kramer to the Lions, then brought in Marv Fleming, younger and faster than Kramer, as a replacement. The problem of a dependable place-kicker seemed to be solved with the acquisition of Don Chandler from the New York Giants.

The Packers opened the season with four straight victories, including a win over the Baltimore Colts, champions of the Western Conference the year before.

The string also included a victory over San Francisco. The game contained an interesting footnote to

Bart's career, one that gives evidence to his amazing pass-throwing accuracy.

During the season before, Bart had begun a record-setting streak of pass attempts without suffering an interception. Early in 1965, Bart topped the mark—208—set by Milt Plum in 1959 and 1960. Every time after that that Bart threw the ball, he set a record.

On October 10, 1965, the long streak came to an end when one of Bart's passes was intercepted by Jim Johnson of the 49ers. Bart's remarkable achievement won him these lines of type in the official record manual of the National Football League:

> "Most Consecutive Passes Attempted, None Intercepted:
> 294 Bryan (Bart) Starr, Green Bay, 1964–1965."

Following San Francisco, the Packers went to Detroit for a game against the Lions. The contest stands as a striking example of Starr's virtuosity.

The Packers were badly outplayed during the first half and went into the locker room with the score 21–3, Detroit.

It had been a very long time since any team had treated the Packers in such rowdy fashion. Their pride was hurt. "We came to Detroit wanting to beat the Lions very badly," Bart said after. "We just couldn't afford to be so bad."

The Packers aroused their fallen spirits and roared from the dressing room with renewed determination. The blocking suddenly improved, and Bart had time to target on his receivers. Bob Long got loose, and Bart hit him with a long spiral for a touchdown. The play covered 62 yards. Shortly after, Bart connected with Tom Moore for another touchdown. The Packers were drawing close. Detroit still led, but by only four points, 21–17.

Play was still in the third period when Bart found himself faced with third down and 2 yards to go on his own 23-yard line. The Lions, looking for a plunge into the line, drew in their defense. The huge crowd began to chant, "Hold that line! Hold that line!"

At the snap, the Detroit line surged in to meet the rush. Bart coolly faked to Taylor, then darted back with the ball. Carroll Dale was wide open, and Bart's pass was perfect. Dale didn't stop running until he reached the end zone. Now the Packers were ahead, 24–21.

Bart delivered the clincher himself in the final period, skirting right end for 4 yards and another touchdown that built the Packer lead to ten points, 31–21. Not long after, the game ended.

The Packers' miraculous comeback put the Detroit players in a state of shock. Big Alex Karras sat on a stool in front of his locker, shaking his head sadly. "There's no way," he said, "no way they could beat us when we were ahead twenty-one to three at the half. I can't believe it. I just can't believe it."

In the Packers' dressing room, Bart's bold third-quarter, third-down pass to Carroll Dale was the subject under dicussion. One pressbox observer called it "a masterpiece of choice and execution."

"It was a great call," said Dale. "Our field position called for a run, and their defense was looking for it. Their cornerback rushed by me, right by me. I just stepped behind him, delayed a second, and then took off. I didn't make a great catch. Bart had it right there."

The Packers' bus was waiting to take the team to the airport, and Bart had to dress hurriedly. He was knotting his tie as a reporter asked him about the pass to Dale.

"We've had success with the same play before," said Bart. "There's nothing new about it."

There was no mirror in the locker room, and each time Bart knotted his tie, the back end kept coming out longer than the front.

"Wasn't that call a bit reckless?" the reporter asked. "You're supposed to be a conservative quarterback."

Bart grinned. "Every once in a while I like to fool 'em," he said.

Bart then grabbed his bag and ran for the bus. The Detroit game was a closed chapter.

The Packers outpointed the Cowboys the next week and then went to Wrigley Field for a meeting with the Bears. In the first quarter, Green Bay launched a touchdown drive. The ball was on the Chicago 47-yard line. It was third down. Bart took off and sprinted downfield. Suddenly Bear safety Roosevelt Taylor came out of nowhere to lower the boom on Bart. Bart got to his feet and started for the huddle, then collapsed. The next thing he knew he was sitting on the bench, and the team doctor was waving a bottle of smelling salts beneath his nose.

Bart gamely went back into the game the next time the Packers got the ball. But his shoulder was throbbing with pain, and he could not pass with his usual effectiveness. "Bart was very sharp when he started," Lombardi said after, "but he could not retain this edge." The Packers lost, 31–10.

Bart was back the next week, but there must have been many moments he wished he hadn't left the locker room. He was dropped eight times for losses. The Packers lost again.

It was developing into a frustrating season. Another second-place finish was beginning to loom. The Colts, after their early-season loss to the Packers, had won every game.

Just as upsetting was the fact that the Packers were not playing sharp, crisp football. On running plays, one man always seemed to release his block, and the opposition would break through to halt the play. There were lapses in the pass blocking, too, and frequently Bart did not get the extra split second he required to get the ball away.

As the title race entered the home stretch, the Packers were 9–3, a record that put them a half a game behind the Colts.

The Packers met the Conference leaders on the next to last weekend of the season. Instead of practicing in frigid Green Bay, Lombardi set up a training camp at

Gaithersburg, Maryland. There the players had to live by the clock. Lombardi made nightly bed checks.

Away from all distractions, the Packers worked hard. Their ability to execute sharpened. Their spirit began to build. The team was bursting with confidence when they took the field at Municipal Stadium.

The Colts never knew what hit them. Paul Hornung had one of the best days of his career, scoring five touchdowns, two of them on passes from Bart. Bart also passed to Dowler for a touchdown, as the Packers won, 42–27.

The game lifted Green Bay into first place in the Western Conference, but the next week they slipped back into a tie with the Colts by failing to beat the 49ers in San Francisco. So it was back to Lambeau Stadium for a play-off game with the Colts.

Bart has good reason to remember the play-off, first of all, because the Packers won. And second of all, because of one play—the first play from scrimmage.

Starr, electing to pass, dropped back into the pocket. Bill Anderson was to be the receiver. Bart's throw, a short spiral, was perfect. But before Anderson could get a firm grip on the ball, he was hit by Lenny Lyles, and the ball jarred loose. Dan Shinnick of the Colts scooped up the ball on the Packer 25-yard line and started down the sideline for the Green Bay goal. Two brawny blockers led the way.

Only Bart stood between Shinnick and the goal. Bart moved into position, hoping to drive Shinnick out of bounds. Suddenly—*crash!* The Colts' Jerry Logan hit Bart with a devastating block. Bart fell to the ground writhing in pain, his hands clutching his side. Shinnick romped into the end zone.

On the sidelines, the team doctor found that Logan's block had loosened several of Bart's ribs. The pain was so intense that Bart couldn't raise his right arm high enough to take off his helmet, much less throw the ball.

Bart was through for the day. Into the game came Zeke Bratkowski, the Packers' backup quarterback.

The Colts were also without their starting quarterback, Johnny Unitas. He could not play because of a leg injury. Gary Cuozzo, the Colts' No. 2 man, was also *hors de combat*. The desperate Colts were forced to use Tom Matte, a halfback, as their signal caller.

Bratkowski was often called the best "relief pitcher" in the National Football League. He had the ability to take command and lead the team whenever Bart was out.

"Bart and I are close friends, not rivals," Bratkowski said more than once. "We try to help each other out, and rivalry never enters our minds. We're a team, and that's the only way to approach this game."

Starr has always enjoyed a splendid relationship with his backups, with Green Bay's No. 2 quarterbacks.

After Lamar McHan was traded away in 1961, Green Bay obtained John Roach from the St. Louis Cardinals to understudy Bart. When Bart broke his hand and was sidelined for a month in 1963, Roach filled in brilliantly. The Packers had only one quarterback during this period, so they made a trade to obtain

Zeke Bratkowski. Roach then retired, and Bratkowski became the backup man.

Occasionally quarterbacks on a team become involved in heated rivalry for the No. 1 slot. Sometimes there is grumbling and jealousy as a result. The team becomes divided into two cliques, each one supporting its own man. Teams afflicted with this type of dissension seldom perform well.

But this never happened at Green Bay.

Starr and Bratkowski became close friends. Each was always the booster of the other. They often studied movies together at Bart's home. They were quick to give each other suggestions and ideas on how to improve. They each had a sincere desire to help the other in the development of their respective skills.

Whenever Bart had the opportunity, he paid tribute to Bratkowski's talents. "You don't know what a help it is to have a man of Zeke's experience on the phones when I come to the sideline," Bart has said more than once. "He'll tell me things like, 'You haven't used a draw yet today,' or 'You haven't called such and such a pass that should work against their defense.' Things like that. He sees things that I don't see and helps me from getting in a rut."

Bratkowski admitted that he had often tried to pattern his style of play after Starr's. Sometimes opposing players could notice no difference when Bratkowski came in as Bart's replacement.

In the play-off game against the Colts, Bratkowski put on another Starrlike performance.

With the Packers behind, 10–0, in the third period,

Zeke brought the team back, passing to Carroll Dale to set up Green Bay's first touchdown. Later Bratkowski directed the team to within 27 yards of the Baltimore goal. Don Chandler came in and booted a field goal, and it sent the game into sudden-death overtime.

After the Colts had missed a field goal, Zeke steered the Packers to the Baltimore 25-yard line. Again Chandler kicked. Again it was good.

After two seasons of frustration, the Packers were Western Conference champions once more.

Now it was the following Sunday, and the Packers were playing the Cleveland Browns for the National League title. All week long the newspapers had asked, "Will Bart Starr start?"

Lombardi did not answer the question until just before game time. After watching Bart throw, he felt Starr could do the job. And a brief conference with Bart confirmed the fact.

Cleveland had won the Eastern Conference championship without too much trouble. They featured a devastating ground game, spearheaded by Jimmy Brown, pro football's best running back, bar none.

The Green Bay weather was up to form. It was a cold and dreary day, and it snowed during the morning of game day. The field became a quagmire.

Bart had studied Cleveland films, and he had been briefed by Lombardi and the other coaches. He knew what to expect from Cleveland's defenses. They played a cute "lie back and don't give them a long gainer" type of game. When opponents got in close, the Brown defensemen bunched up to stop them.

When Bart saw the Cleveland players hanging deep, he punctured their defenses with short passes. Time and time again he threw.

When the Browns adjusted to stop the short tosses, Bart went to something else. He sent Carroll Dale slanting out to the left. In streaked the Cleveland cornerback to cover. Dale paused for a split second, then looped behind the defenseman and sped downfield. Too late the Browns realized they had been outfoxed. Bart's pass was right on target, and the Packers had the game's first touchdown. Chandler's kick made the score 7–0.

After that, the Cleveland defense became much more cautious. Bart had hurt them once. They would not let him do it again. Bart went back to riddling the defense with short passes, and he also concentrated on thrusts into the line and around the ends, with Hornung and Taylor doing the carrying.

Meanwhile, the Packer defense, plus the muddy going, held Jimmy Brown. He was to be held to 50 yards for the day. Hornung and Taylor were to total 201 yards.

Green Bay's superiority became clear in the third quarter. They led, 20–12, at the end of the period.

In the fourth quarter, Bart switched to a ball-control game. The only scoring of the period came on a field goal by Don Chandler. The Packers won, 23–12.

To many of the Packers, the 1965 championship was the most satisfying of all. They had overcome more than the usual amount of obstacles to win—the injuries, the seeming lack of team spirit in midseason, and the play-off game against the Colts.

Bart wore a smile of fulfillment as he stripped off his mud-stained uniform. Shouts of glee and rollicking laughter exploded all around him.

Bart looked at his exultant teammates, then flashed a broad grin. "You know, it's nice," he said, "nice to be back on top, to be back where we belong."

10

Bart Starr of Chateau Drive

DURING MOST OF HIS YEARS with the Packers, Bart, his wife, and their two young sons—Bart, Jr., and Bret—lived in a modest ranch house on Chateau Drive, about half a mile from Lambeau Field in Green Bay. From his front door, Bart could see the stadium.

A basketball hoop was mounted on one side of the garage. Bart, Jr., who was born in 1958, often shot baskets with his friends. Sometimes Bart, Sr., would join in the game. In most cities, boys would be awed by the presence of an NFL superstar. But not in Green Bay. Bart, Sr., is accepted in the same way any other father in the neighborhood would be.

One day the Green Bay *Press-Gazette* assigned a reporter to interview the families who lived near Bart Starr. Lee Wagner, the interviewer, found that Bart was thought of merely as the man who lives across the street. He might be a druggist or a salesman. "He's accepted here as a neighbor, not as a celebrity," said Robert Steward. "We'd hate to lose him as a neighbor."

Naturally, everyone in the neighborhood knew who Bart Starr was. During the football season they watched the Packer games on television or from the stands at Lambeau Field, rooting for Bart as he threw passes and directed the team. "But when the football season is over," said Mrs. Marshall Williamson, "he's just Mr. Starr.

"The Starrs are no different from any of our other neighbors. They're just real fine people."

Evenings in the early summer, Bart often joined some of his neighbors on the sidewalk for conversation. The subject was seldom football. "We don't talk about football because we figure that everybody who approaches Bart wants to talk about football," said Robert Steward. "We talk about the lawn, and the neighborhood, and the city—things like that."

During the winter a number of Bart's neighbors were likely to call on him to borrow his snowblower. "My son," said Steward, "usually takes care of Bart's sidewalk during the winter. And then Bart lets him bring the snowblower over here and take care of our walk."

Lee Wagner drew these conclusions about Bart Starr of Chateau Drive: "He's the guy who, along with his wife, joins the neighborhood gang for a summer Sunday afternoon picnic. He's the guy who offers you the use of his lawn tools when you find yourself confronted with a sticky project. He's the guy who calls to see if your daughter can baby-sit Saturday night."

Occasionally Bart would invite his sons and their friends to jump into the family station wagon, and then it would be off to McDonald's for burgers and malts. Sometimes on rainy days Bart would drive the boys to the YMCA to shoot baskets.

The Starrs worship at the First Methodist Church of Green Bay, and Bart is an active member of the church's governing board. The Reverend Roger Bourland, the church's pastor, describes Bart as a humble person, "but at the same time dynamic and exciting.

"One of his greatest characteristics is that he does so much for people in a personal way with his time, talent, and money. And most of them don't know that he is the one who is responsible."

During the 1967 season, some of the Packers began to hold devotional services for the Protestant members of the team who usually were unable to attend church services when the club was on the road. A few hours before the game, the group would meet and read from the Bible, say a few prayers, and there would be a short discussion. About twenty team members attended. The services were always conducted by one of two men. One was Carroll Dale. The other was Bart Starr.

Bart is extremely active in community affairs. He is the fund-drive chairman for the 700-acre Rawhide Ranch in New London, Wisconsin. Described as a combination church, camp, and marine boot camp, it offers leadership training for underprivileged teen-age boys of the state of Wisconsin.

In 1967, when *Sport* magazine awarded Bart an expensive sports car for being named the Most Valuable Player in the Super Bowl, Bart promptly donated the automobile to Rawhide Ranch. It was used as a raffle prize and earned $45,000.

Bart is also a member of the Green Bay Downtown Redevelopment Authority, an organization that is working to improve the appearance of the downtown area of the city. Bart often makes calls upon officials of local companies, inviting them to help the Authority to achieve its goals.

Bart maintains more than a passing interest in national affairs. During the Presidential campaign of 1968, Bart worked for Richard Nixon. Starr first met Nixon in 1957 at the dedication ceremonies for Green Bay's new stadium. He was then the Vice President. They met several times after that. "I like him, and I think he'd make a great President," Bart said in 1968. "He's honest, dedicated, and experienced."

During the off season, Bart sometimes speaks before groups of youngsters. He tells them of the beliefs that have helped shape his life.

"Always play to win," he says. "Winning isn't everything, but putting forth the effort to win *is everything*.

"Winning requires teamwork. And teamwork requires that each member of the team perform his assignment to the best of his ability.

"The winning effort, winning teamwork, a winning

performance—they all require proper instruction. Listen, learn, and follow instructions. Only then can you turn in a winning performance."

Bart does not smoke. He seldom takes a drink. He will not allow his name to be used in cigarette or liquor advertising. "Hell" and "damn" creep into his conversation only occasionally.

One day in a game against Chicago, the Bears' linebacker Bill George was found lying on the ground laughing when the play ended. The Packers had eluded George for a sizable gain.

"What's so funny?" one of George's teammates asked.

"I cussed at Starr," said George, still laughing, "and I'll be darned if he didn't cuss back at me. It's the first time I ever heard him use a swear word. It sounded so funny coming from him that I just broke up."

Bart is disturbed by magazine and newspaper stories that report on drinking, gambling, and girl chasing on the part of professional athletes. He knows youngsters read the stories and then say to themselves, "Well, if it's all right for him, it's all right for me." Sports heroes, Bart believes, have a grave responsibility to be impeccable in their conduct because they are so idolized by boys.

When he addresses groups of boys, Bart frequently tells them, "A lot of people may think you are a sissy if you don't smoke or drink. Well, I know plenty of pro football players who don't smoke or drink—people like Fran Tarkenton (of the New York Giants) and Bill

Glass (of the Cleveland Browns), and I don't think you would call Fran Tarkenton or Bill Glass a sissy."

Starr ranks as one of the state of Wisconsin's most noted personalities. He has been named Man of the Year by countless business and civic groups. There is said to be a $100,000-a-year job as a stockbroker waiting for him in Milwaukee as soon as he decides to retire from football.

Someone once asked Jerry Kramer, the onetime Packer guard, if there was anybody he could think of in football or out who didn't like Bart Starr.

"Not a person," Kramer answered. Then he grinned. "Except maybe me.

"Sometimes he gets on my nerves because he's just too perfect."

11

Secrets of Quarterbacking

IN TALKING WITH YOUNG quarterbacks, in the football clinics he conducts, and in his book *Quarterbacking,* Bart Starr gives meaningful tips on how to play pro football's most difficult and demanding position. But there is no better way to learn the fundamentals of the game than to watch Bart in action.

When Bart positions himself to receive the ball from the center, he plants his feet solidly, bends his knees slightly, and leans forward from the waist. He places his right hand, palm down, under the seat of the center, applying firm and steady pressure. Bart then brings his left hand, palm up, into position, so that the thumb of the left hand touches the thumb of the right. The hands work together to trap the ball as it comes from the center. Bart and his center practice constantly to develop a flawless exchange.

As soon as Bart receives the ball, he brings it in tight to his belly. This helps prevent a fumble. As he turns to hand off the ball, Bart moves with short, quick steps. He focuses his eyes on his target—the back's hands and forearms positioned at his belly. Bart realizes it is the quarterback's responsibility to avoid a fumble as the ball is exchanged. The hand-off itself is firm and crisp.

Bart calls out signals in a voice that is loud and clear. This helps boost the confidence of the team, he believes. Bart's wife says that he is a Jekyll and Hyde as far as his voice is concerned, that he is not very loud around the house, but when he is on the field, she can hear him barking out signals as far back as the fiftieth row of the stadium.

Bart fakes hand-offs with either the ball or his hand. In using the ball, he tucks his elbows to his side and grips the ball firmly with both hands. He hands it to the back, then takes it away. In the hand fake, Bart conceals the ball at his side or midsection, then gives the back an empty hand. "If you learn to fake well," Bart says, "it's almost the same as having an extra blocker or two."

Bart names Babe Parilli as "the finest faker I have ever seen." Parilli played his college football at the University of Kentucky and with four different professional teams before landing with the New York Jets in 1967 as backup quarterback to Joe Namath. Parilli, as a college player, impressed Bart with his fast hands and his ability to keep his elbows tight to his body, thus camouflaging his movement of the ball. "He was a real sleight of hand artist," Bart declares.

When Bart pitches out to a back, he steps into the direction he intends the ball to follow, then flips a soft, feathery toss. Using either one hand or two—he recommends two hands for young quarterbacks—he leads the back with the ball.

Bart is a pocket passer. He drops back behind his cup of blockers, looks, then throws. Of course, once in a while the protection breaks down and Bart must scramble—scurry about in the backfield while searching for an open man to throw to. "You get forced into that once every so often," Bart says, "but I sure wouldn't want to make my living as a scrambler."

When setting up to pass, Bart goes back with short, quick steps. He's lightning-fast. He never turns his back on the defense; otherwise, he might fail to see how the defense is shifting to guard against the pass. In addition, he would lose sight of his receivers, and it would be difficult to pick them up again. He goes back a distance of 7 to 8 yards into the protective pocket.

The left hand plays two important roles. Bart steadies the ball with his left hand as he darts back, and then, as he passes, he stretches it outward from his body to help maintain his balance.

When passing, Bart grips the football firmly but never squeezes it. His throwing hand is positioned slightly in back of the ball's center. His fingers are spread apart with the fourth and little fingers crossing the lacing.

Bart, like virtually all pro quarterbacks, throws overhand. As he brings the ball through, he takes a short step forward with his left foot and shifts his weight to it. He snaps his wrist at the finish and follows through with both his arm and body.

Often young quarterbacks ask Bart, "How do I achieve a spiral?"

"Just work on a delivery that is natural," Bart says. "Be careful not to push the ball. Give it a lot of finger action as you deliver. The spiral will take care of itself."

Bart recommends that young passers concentrate on accuracy. "Distance is secondary," he says.

Each of Bart's three principal receivers—the split end, the tight end, and the flanker—can run as many

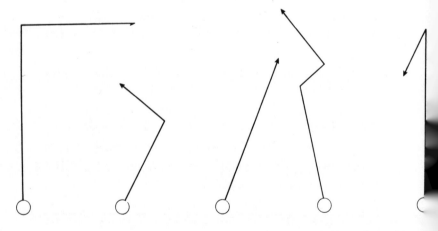

as twenty individual patterns or routes. A handful of them are shown on this page. (They are, from left to right, a square-out, vee-in, slant, zig-in, and come-back.) If all combinations of patterns were considered for each of the three receivers, the number of possible plays would number in the thousands.

Of course, no team tries to master them all. They concentrate on certain ones, with the receivers running complementary patterns. Suppose the split end runs a hitch or slant pattern, going only 5 or 6 yards downfield. Then the flanker will run a deep pattern. Or if the tight end runs a deep hook, then the flanker may run a short corner pattern or a post.

When Bart goes back to throw, he frequently looks first to his left, usually the short man. If this receiver is covered, he then looks right, to his tight end. Last, he looks for his flanker.

"One mark of a good quarterback," says Bart, "is the ability to locate an alternate receiver when the primary receiver is covered." Once he spots the open man, the quarterback has to be able to shuffle his feet around in a hurry to get in a position to throw in the new direction.

One of the first things that Vince Lombardi did after becoming Green Bay's coach was to alter the Packers' passing game. He introduced innovations that made it possible for Bart to complete passes against virtually every type of defense.

In the days before Lombardi, Starr might call a fly pattern—a long pass with the receiver breaking straight downfield—and midway in the play he would see that the opposition safety had closed off the fly route. In other words, the defense had the play beaten. If Bart threw the ball, it would be batted down or, worse, intercepted.

But Lombardi instructed the receivers to vary their

routes slightly when they encountered a defense that threatened to beat the play. This system, however, increased the pressure on Bart, for he had to be able to perceive how the receivers might be altering their patterns.

Bart developed this skill through long hours on the practice field where he worked with his receivers on timing and "keys"—the slight movements on the part of the receivers that serve to signal speed and direction. "No passing attack," says Starr, "can be successful unless a close mutual understanding exists between passer and receiver."

Each member of every professional team is issued a play book, a conventional three-ring looseleaf binder with a cloth cover, the type any schoolboy is likely to carry. It is crammed with diagrams of the team's plays and its basic offensive and defensive formations.

From the time the player arrives at training camp in July until the end of the season, he is never far from his play book. He carries it with him to classroom meetings, and he studies it at night. It is his reading matter on the plane when the team travels.

The play book must be turned in to the club at the end of the season. Losing a play book means a costly fine.

From team to team in professional football, there is sometimes a slight difference in the meaning of the game's technical terms. To avoid confusion, the play book begins with a glossary. Here are some of the terms that appear in the Green Bay play book:

OFF SIDE—the side away from which the play is called.

ON SIDE—the side to which the play is called.

STRONG SIDE—the side on which the flanker is set.

WEAK SIDE—the side opposite to which the flanker is set.

WING—any flanking back.

SLOT—a flanking back who is set inside the split end.

PINCH BLOCK—to double-team one man.

FLY—a pass pattern straight downfield at full speed.

For each game the coaches develop a game plan, the main feature of which is a "ready list," a rundown of about thirty plays the coaches believe will work against the types of defenses the opposition has used in recent games.

Because, like every quarterback, he handles the ball on every play, Starr must absorb the game plan the way a sponge takes up water. Not only must he know everyone's assignment on every play, he must know the enemy, be aware of the skills and shortcomings of each one of the opposition players.

One of Bart's favorite pass patterns is diagramed on the following page. It can be thrown against virtually any type of defense. It offers Bart four possible receivers— the split end (SE), the tight end (TE), the flanker (FL), or the fullback (FB).

The flanker has a variety of routes that he can run off his basic pattern. He can cut in, out, or back. Or he

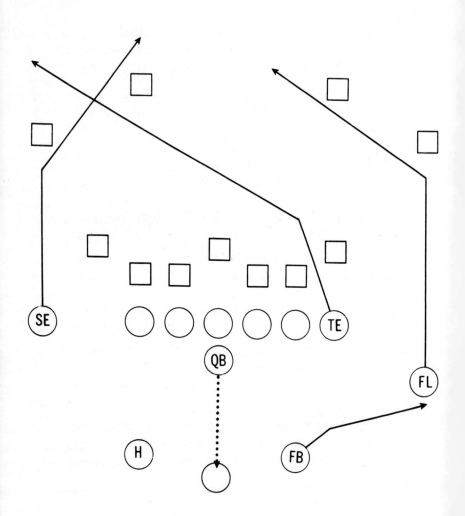

can stop dead, then streak downfield for a long pass. The fullback is the safety valve. If all the other receivers are covered, he is the one who will get the ball. If a blitz is on, however, the fullback must remain back and pick up his linebacker.

The blocking is conventional. The center is responsible for the middle linebacker. The left halfback is responsible for the linebacker shooting in from his side. The guards and tackles drop back to form a protective pocket from which the quarterback delivers the ball.

The play-action pass (following page) is another play that Bart likes to call. He often uses is on third down, with Boyd Dowler his target.

The Packers set up as if to run, with Dowler moved in tight from his spread-end position. This makes the defense think that he is going to block on a running play. But on the snap, Dowler drives into the linebacker, holds the block for a two count, and then streaks straight downfield.

Bart, meanwhile, fakes a hand-off to the fullback slanting toward the left tackle slot, then drops back to pass.

The deep defensive men—the cornerback and the safety on the left side—dart in to stop the running, whereupon Dowler breaks downfield behind them. Bart then has one of his favorite receivers touchdown-bound.

In "must-yardage" situations, Bart frequently relies upon Green Bay's famed power sweep (diagrammed on page 132). During the mid-1960's, it was known as Green Bay's bread-and-butter play. It typified the pow-

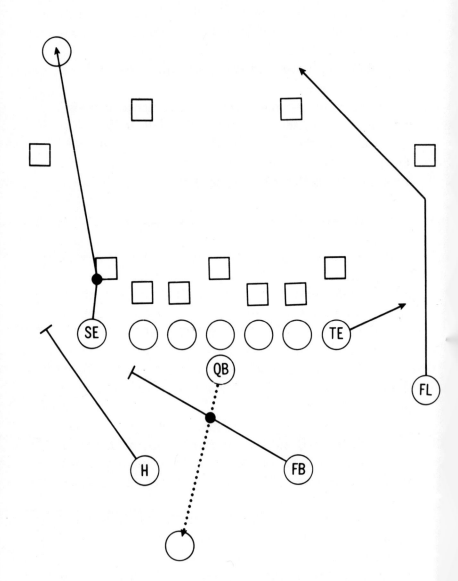

erful, hard-nosed style of football that the team was noted for under Vince Lombardi. The power sweep involves no hocus-pocus. Its success is based upon execution, particularly upon the ability of the blockers to clear the flank for the sweeping back.

"It takes strong-legged backs such as Jimmy Taylor and Paul Hornung to run it," Lombardi once said, "plus real fine offensive guards to lead it." After Taylor and Hornung had left Green Bay, the play functioned with Donny Anderson as halfback and Jim Grabowski as fullback.

Starr has the option of calling the sweep to the right or left. In the example above, it is run to the right. The left guard must pull from the line and run laterally to the right to join the other guard to form a convoy of blockers. The fullback drives through the line to block out the defensive end. The tight end's assignment is to hook the linebacker to the inside.

Starr hands off to the halfback, who clears right end and heads downfield.

The sweep is used not only as the Packers' "money" play, but also to help establish a running game and make Bart's passing more effective. The sweep is used, too, when the Packers are leading in a game and Starr wishes to run out the clock. On any play when the ball carrier sweeps wide, as much as a minute of playing time can be consumed.

Bart, like all pro quarterbacks, must be able to read enemy defenses the way most people read a calendar. When he steps up to the line of scrimmage and sees that the defense is set to stop the play he has called in

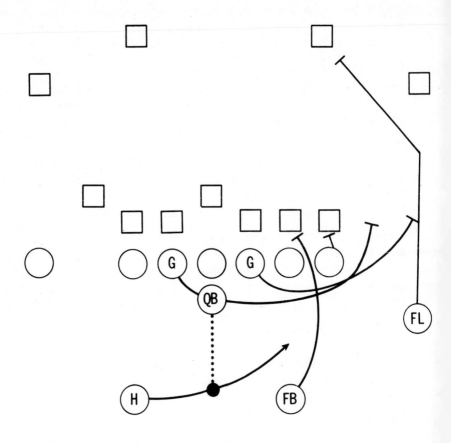

the huddle, the quarterback calls an automatic (sometimes called an audible), a signal to the team that he is
changing the play.

It is a complicated piece of business. It works like
this: Suppose Bart wants to run the Packers' 49 sweep,
a play for which the team has become famous. In the
huddle, Bart may say, "Red right, forty-nine, on three."

"Red" is a code word indicating how the backs are

to position themselves. The Packers use red, brown, and blue formations. When lined up in the red formation, the backs are split, one behind each tackle.

"Right" is a signal to the tight end. It means he is to line up on the right side.

The number "forty-nine" means that the No. 4 back, the running back positioned to the left, is to take the ball into the No. 9 hole, located outside right end.

The words "on three" are a signal to the team that the ball is going to be snapped the third time Bart says "Hut."

So far it is simple. Now suppose that when the team breaks from the huddle, Bart notices that the defense is arrayed to stop the 49 sweep. As he bends to take the ball from the center, he calls an automatic. "Three . . . forty-six . . . hut! . . . Hut!" he might say.

The team knows that if the first number Bart calls is the same as the snap signal given in the huddle—three, in this case—the play is off. The new play is the number that follows—forty-six, a signal that the No. 4 back is going into the No. 6 hole, between left tackle and left end.

What is remarkable about all this is that it happens so quickly. Within the space of just a few seconds, Bart, in the huddle, calls a play he judges to be right for the situation, setting his backs and receivers in proper formation. Then he sees the play won't work, so he calls a new play, one designed to take advantage of a weakness in the opposition defense.

It sounds complex. But to Bart, and to other skilled

play callers, it's all just about as natural as stirring morning coffee.

It was Vince Lombardi who taught Bart the value of automatics. "Why bat your head against a stone wall?" he said to Starr not long after he had taken over the coaching duties. "Every defense has a weak point. That's where to hit."

The 1961 title game between the Packers and the Giants illustrates this point. New York unveiled an unbalanced line intended to cut off Taylor's wide sweeps. But the formation rendered the Giants vulnerable to quick pops—driving runs at the linebacker.

Sam Huff was often the victim. "We ran at Huff four and five yards all day long," Starr recalls.

The Giants adjusted by moving Huff farther to the right, but this made it difficult for him to cover passes on the left. "Anytime you make a change, you have to give up something," Starr said. "We try to find that something."

P.S. The Packers won the game, 37–0.

The cat and mouse game that Bart plays with the opposing line has become much more difficult than it used to be. "Defenses are improving," Bart noted in mid-1968. "The men are bigger, faster, and smarter. You don't find glaring weaknesses to exploit anymore.

"Some years ago you could read coverages like a book. Not anymore. They line up and show you one thing, then move into something else on the snap of the ball."

Thus, the value of audibles has dwindled. "You audible something," Bart declared, "and you get fooled. It's become a real guessing game."

Like all pro quarterbacks, Starr consults with his coach and the assistant coaches throughout a game. When a time-out is called, he will trot to the sideline to talk to Coach Bengston.

"This is done mainly to help us collect our thoughts," Starr says. "We may have run a play once or twice that has failed. Now I want to try it again. I ask the coach's advice. It's helpful to get his opinion, especially if the play could mean the difference between losing and winning."

Sometimes, however, the coach is not of very great aid. During the 1961 season in a game against the Vikings, the Packers had drawn three consecutive 15-yard penalties. Bart found himself faced with an incredible third-down and 50-yards-to-go situation.

Bart was stumped. His teammates could offer no help. Then he looked toward the sideline where Lombardi was standing.

"Lombardi," Starr recalls, "just shrugged. He was baffled, too."

When Bart speaks to young quarterbacks, he never fails to stress the importance of being physically fit. "You must be peaked to the best physical condition possible," he declares.

Physical fitness was almost a mania with Vince Lombardi. When he coached the Packers, he was noted for his "grass drill," a grueling up-down exercise. "Down!" Lombardi would shout, and the players would fall to the ground. "Up!" he would then command, and the players would spring to their feet. Lombardi would repeat this exercise sixty or seventy times or, as one player recalls, "until we were all ready to die."

For young quarterbacks, Bart suggests exercises a bit less demanding. He says that push-ups are excellent for a quarterback because they help develop shoulder and arm muscles. To build endurance, Bart suggests running up and down stadium steps, or any type of stairs. Before he goes to training camp in July, Bart practices with a weighted training football to get his throwing arm in shape.

Bart, who is 6 feet 1 inch ("almost six feet two" he says) and weighs 200 pounds, feels that quarterbacks of the present day must have good height. This is because defensive personnel are taller than they used to be, ranging up to 6 feet 5 inches and even beyond. A quarterback has to be able to get the ball over them.

In addition to the physical attributes the position demands, and the technical knowledge required, a quarterback must display certain qualities of leadership in order to be successful. Dedication is one of the foremost of these qualities. "You must possess a burning devotion and desire to suceed," Bart declares in *Quarterbacking*, "or you will not succeed."

Poise is another vital quality. During the 1962 season, the Packers were playing the Lions, and the game was in its last minute. Bart, upset by the fact that the Packers were losing, took his frustration out on an official. He yelled at referee Red Pace, "Hey, ref, if you give us any more of those lousy calls, I'm going to reach out and bite that big, fat head of yours right off."

Pace looked Bart square in the eye. "Starr," he said,

"if you do, you'll be the only quarterback in the league with more brains in his stomach than in his head."

The Packer bench, Bart recalls, became convulsed with laughter. "That cured me of losing my poise," Bart says.

Poise comes with confidence, a quality, says Bart, that can be developed on the practice field. Bart cites Paul Hornung as one of the Packers' most effective leaders. Bart remembers him as a "lighthearted, carefree kind of guy, with supreme self-confidence."

Courage is another quality a quarterback requires in order to become an effective leader. Getting knocked around is one of the occupational hazards of being a quarterback, Bart says. A player must have courage enough to stand there and take it.

Self-discipline is another quality that leaders display. "If you are not willing to discipline yourself, you can't hope to lead others," Bart states.

"Everybody has leadership potential," says Bart. "But not everyone can get a chance to express this ability. I've been lucky," Bart declares. "I've gotten that chance."

12

Super Bowl

THE AMERICAN FOOTBALL LEAGUE, backed by a pair of Texas millionaires, set up shop in the fall of 1959. Almost immediately pro football fans began asking when the AFL would play the NFL in a championship game.

The American League spurred interest in the idea by issuing a yearly challenge to its older, richer rival, but the National League ignored the offers. They did until 1966, that is. That year representatives of the two leagues sat down and worked out a merger agreement. One of the provisions was a title game between the champions of each league. Someone labeled the contest the Super Bowl, and the name stuck.

"The Packers felt," said Starr, "that if anybody was going to represent the National League it should be us.

The tradition of forty years of football dictated it. The success and stature that we had achieved since the arrival of Coach Lombardi said we should be that team.

"But saying it and getting there are two different things."

The Packers were the choice of the experts to win the Western Conference, and they lived up to expectations. They lost only two of fourteen games—by a total of four points. They finished the season with a string of five straight wins and clinched the title with a 14–10 victory over Baltimore in the thirteenth game of the season.

Dallas had won the Eastern Conference championship. Now only the Cowboys stood between the Packers and their hopes of "getting there."

To escape Green Bay's Arctic weather, Lombardi took the Packers to Tulsa, Oklahoma, for several days of pregame workouts. But when the team arrived, they were greeted with snow and freezing rain.

Lombardi did not allow the bad weather to interfere with his plans. Each day followed this schedule: 8 A.M., breakfast; 10 A.M. to 11:30 A.M., team scrimmage; 12:30 P.M., lunch; 3 P.M., team meeting; 6 P.M., dinner; 7:30 P.M., team meeting. The evening sessions were given over to a discussion of the game plan.

On the day of the game, more than 72,000 fans jammed the Cotton Bowl in Dallas, including 3,500 of the Packers' most loyal supporters who had made the long trek from Green Bay.

Lombardi gave Bart a special play to open the game. It worked to perfection. Bart handed off to halfback Elijah Pitts. As soon as he penetrated the line of scrimmage, Pitts cut sharply to his right and then headed downfield, ripping off 32 yards.

"An electric feeling surged through the team," Bart said after. "We knew we were going to score."

Six plays later the Packers were on the Cowboy 17-yard line. Dallas was looking for a run, but Bart crossed them up, arching a pass over the middle to Elijah Pitts. Touchdown!

On the kickoff that followed, Mel Renfro of the Cowboys fumbled. Jim Grabowski picked up the loose ball and galloped into the end zone. After less than five minutes of play, the Packers were ahead, 14–0.

The Cowboys, because of their youth and inexperience in championship play, might well have collapsed at this point. But they didn't. They blazed back, tying the game at 14–14.

In the second period, Bart threw 51 yards to Carroll Dale. Up went Dale for the ball. Up, too, went Cornell Green, the Dallas defensive man. But Green jumped a split second too soon, and the ball eluded his grasping fingers and settled into Dale's waiting arms. Dale scored to put the Packers ahead, 21–14.

But the Cowboys would not quit. They answered back with a field goal, cutting the Green Bay lead to 4 points, 21–17.

Then early in the third period, the Cowboys turned a Packer fumble into a field goal. Suddenly the Green Bay margin was only 1 point. Throughout the season, no team had been able to rip into the Packer defense the way the Cowboys were doing.

But Bart contrived to tip the scales in Green Bay's favor once again. The Packers had the ball on the Cowboy 16. Bart scampered back to pass. In bolted Chuck Howley, Dallas' All-League linebacker. His arms encircled Bart's ankles like a steel trap. He squeezed; Bart started to fall. But as he was going down, Bart spotted Boyd Dowler in the end zone. Somehow Bart got the ball away and also managed to hit the bull's-eye with it. The Packers now led, 28–20.

Bart put on a masterful performance in the fourth quarter. The ball was on the Green Bay 45-yard line, third down and 19. Bart scrambled back, cocked his arm, and fired, hitting Marv Fleming for 24 yards and a first down.

Moments later Bart was faced with another perilous situation—third and 12. He called another pass, this time with Jimmy Taylor his target. Perfection again. The play got the team 16 yards and another first down.

Two plays later the ball was on the Dallas 28-yard line. It was another third-down situation. Nineteen yards were needed for a first down. Could Bart come through again? He called another pass. Just before the team broke from the huddle, McGee spoke to Bart. "I'd like to change my pattern," he whispered. "I'd like to run a zig-out. I think I can beat my man with it."

Bart nodded. He took the snap and drifted back. He saw McGee, saw him slant downfield, cut left abruptly, then suddenly break right and then toward the end zone. He was wide open.

Bart reared back and let go, whizzing a faultless spiral to the streaking McGee. Without breaking stride, McGee brought the ball to his chest and stepped into the end zone with it.

The Packers now led, 34–20. There were less than six minutes remaining.

The Cowboys were down but still not out. Don Meredith uncorked a 68-yard touchdown pass to Frank Clarke. The gap was narrowed to 7 points. The crowd was in a frenzy. They knew that a touchdown and an extra point would send the game into sudden-death overtime.

Bart, to counter the Cowboys' blitz, came out throwing the ball. He got two first downs, but in a third and 7 situation, the Cowboys trapped Taylor behind the line of scrimmage on a screen pass.

Don Chandler's punt trickled off the side of his foot and went out of bounds on the Green Bay 47. About four minutes were left. The fans were delirious.

Bart, on the sidelines, watched Meredith march his team toward the Packer end zone, the prelude to one of the most bizarre endings any championship game has known.

A long pass and then a pass interference penalty put the ball on the Green Bay 2-yard line. A minute and fifty-two seconds were left to play, plenty of time to score the tying touchdown. The massive crowd, realizing this, was on its feet and screaming.

But Green Bay would not be beaten. Later, line-backer Lee Roy Caffey was to say, "We got together in the defensive huddle and vowed we would not let the offensive team down. Bart Starr had called a beautiful game. We weren't going to be the ones to ruin it."

The teams lined up. Meredith handed to Dan Reeves. Thwack! Reeves got a yard, no more.

Now it was second down. The Packers on the sidelines were screaming at their defensive team, telling them to dig in, to hold them.

Meredith started the countdown. A tense Dallas lineman jumped off side. The referee's yellow flag went down, and the Cowboys were penalized back to the 6.

On second down and 6, Meredith threw to Dan Reeves. He got his fingers on the ball, then dropped it. The pressure was telling. On third down, Meredith passed successfully to Pettis Norman, who was smothered by Green Bay tacklers at the 2.

The teams came up to the line of scrimmage. Fourth down, 2 yards to go. The whole season had come down to one play.

Meredith barked the signals. He took the snap and rolled to his right. Was he going to run or pass? Dave Robinson, Green Bay's 250-pound linebacker, didn't wait to find out. He charged in like a guided missile, his long arms upstretched. Meredith threw in desperation. His target, Bob Hayes, was surrounded by green jerseys. Meredith winced as if in deep pain.

The Green Bay safety Tom Brown got his hands on the ball, clasped it to his chest, and fell to the ground in the end zone. A bitter groan went up from the stands. The interception had stopped the Cowboys dead. It was all over.

The Packer bench went wild. It was as if the team had just won its first championship, not its fourth.

Despite the melee on the field, Bart sought out Don Meredith. He shook his rival's hand and praised him for bringing his team back after twice being behind by two touchdowns.

Then Bart turned and ran from the field. Suddenly a bitter memory flashed into his mind. He recalled 1960 and the Packers' championship game against the Philadelphia Eagles. In the game's dying seconds, the Packers had the ball deep in Eagle territory. Victory was within their grasp. But they had been stopped dead—just as the Cowboys had been stopped today.

Bart Starr knew the torture that Don Meredith was suffering. Indeed, no one knew better.

Played on Sunday, January 15, 1967, the first Super Bowl game was truly super. Both networks were to televise the event simultaneously, and an audience of 65,000,000 was expected to watch. The huge Los Angeles Coliseum was the site of the contest.

Each winning player was to receive $15,000, and each loser $7,500. Never had the rewards been so great in any sports event.

But more than money was at stake. There was an element of pride involved, with each team aware that it was carrying the prestige of its respective league.

In the way of reputation, Green Bay had more to lose than Kansas City, much more. The Packers had to win and win big in order to support the National

League's boast that it was pro football's only major league. If the Chiefs were able merely to make the game close, it would dispute that theory.

The Chiefs were an unknown quantity, and preparing for them was a difficult chore. Of course, the Packers had films of previous Kansas City games, but since the Chiefs were always matched against AFL teams, there was no basis for comparison. "We watched the Chiefs on defense against somebody like the Jets or Chargers, and we didn't know anything about the personnel of the Jets or Chargers," Bart noted, "so we didn't know how to rate Kansas City's performance."

As game day dawned, many questions loomed. Would Starr be bewildered by the Chiefs' tricky "triple stack" defense? In this formation, Kansas City deployed their linebackers behind their linemen in such a way that an end was left as an outside floater.

Would this upset Starr, make him lose the continuity of his play calling? Would the great variety of blitzes used by the Chiefs unnerve him?

Trickery also typified the Chief's offense. They liked to start with an I formation and then shift into one of a variety of setups—the slot, the doubled-winged T, or the straight T. Len Dawson, the Chiefs' quarterback, was expected to move around, gaining his protection from a "floating" pocket.

Against all this razzle-dazzle, the Packers were planning to use a standard 4–3 pro defense and a conventional three-end pro offense.

Countless times in the days before the game reporters asked Bart, "What is your prediction on the outcome of the game? Who do you think will win?"

Bart's answer was typical. "I never make predictions. We just go out and play the best we can and hope it's good enough for us to win."

The day of the game dawned California-warm. The field was in perfect condition. There could be no excuses.

The game did not begin as most people thought it would. Starr and the Packers were careful at first, probing and testing the Kansas City defenses.

But the Chiefs were bold, blitzing in past Green Bay blockers. On the Packers' first series of plays, Starr had to hurry a throw to Max McGee, and the ball sailed ten feet over McGee's head. The crowd gasped in surprise.

Another time, in the same series, Buck Buchanan, a mountain of a man at 6 feet 7, 280 pounds, swooped in and pinned Bart to the ground. Bart was dumped a second time on the very next play. Such indignities were not supposed to befall Bart Starr of the Green Bay Packers.

When Bart trotted off the field, his face was calm but his mind was racing. "So they're going with the blitz," he thought. And then the trace of a smile crossed his face.

Bart takes blitzing tactics in stride. Indeed, he says he likes teams to use this weapon. Why? Because when enemy linebackers charge, the other defensive men must resort to man-to-man coverage. To a quarterback of Bart's skill and experience, the man-to-man system presents weaknesses that can be exploited.

As soon as Bart reached the bench, he clasped a pair of headphones to his ears, then spoke into the tiny microphone to one of the assistant coaches posted high atop the stadium. "I think they're leaving themselves open on the right," Bart said.

The coach confirmed this. They then discussed a plan of attack.

Not long after, the Packers got the ball back. It was first and 10 on their own 20.

Bart sent halfback Elijah Pitts into the line for 3 yards. Then Bart darted back with the ball and fired to Marv Fleming who was streaking across the middle. Fleming was tumbled to the ground on the Green Bay 34.

On first down, the blitz was on, and Buchanan blasted in. This time Starr was waiting. He sidestepped the lunging Kansas City lineman and pitched a tight spiral to Pitts. Pitts was tackled at the Kansas City 45. Another first down for Green Bay!

Bart worked the ball to the Kansas City 38-yard line. It was third down and 3.

Starr now knew well what flaws there were in the Chiefs' defenses. On the next play he took advantage of these weaknesses.

As he danced back to throw, Bart watched the play unfold. It was perfect, just as if Lombardi were diagraming it on the blackboard. Max McGee was the intended receiver. McGee raced downfield, then broke inside cornerback Willie Mitchell. Bart threw, Mitchell made a desperate dive to get the ball, but McGee turned and plucked it out of the air, then sprinted into the end zone. Don Chandler booted the extra point, and Green Bay led, 7–0.

Early in the second quarter, the Packers had the ball again. Bart was now convinced that the Chiefs were vulnerable on the flanks, that he could attack successfully with his flanker and split end, that is, with Max McGee and Carroll Dale.

This feeling was confirmed moments later. The Packers had the ball on their own 36-yard line. It was third down. A running play would be the standard call in such a situation, and Jim Taylor was the Packers' favorite runner when short yardage was needed.

Bart took the snap. Taylor charged by. Bart gave him an empty hand. Kansas City cornerback Fred Williamson, suckered by the fake, blazed in to tackle Taylor. Meanwhile, Bart had sent Carroll Dale racing into Williamson's area, and now he looped a long spiral to him. When Dale reached up and gathered it in, no one was within 20 yards of him. It was an easy romp into the end zone. The touchdown was nullified, however, because a Green Bay lineman was illegally in motion, and the play was called back.

Bart was unruffled by this bad break. In eleven plays, he calmly and methodically steered the Packers into the end zone again.

He did it because he was able to come through in the clutch, to deliver on third-down plays. The downfield march included these bits of wizardry:

Third and 5 on the Packer 32: Bart passed complete to McGee for 10 yards and a first down.

Third and 10 on the Packer 42: Bart passed to Dale for 15 yards and a first down.

Third and 5 on the Chiefs' 38: Bart passed to Fleming for 11 yards and a first down.

Third and 7 on the Chiefs' 24: Bart passed to Pitts for 14 yards and a first down.

Bart then called a power sweep. Taylor carried around left end and across the goal line.

Once more Kansas City fought back. But their attack bogged down on the Green Bay 34-yard line, and they had to settle for a field goal.

Seconds later the gun sounded ending the first half. The score was Green Bay, 14; Kansas City, 10.

While Starr had been brilliant, the Packers as a team had not been. They had allowed the Chiefs to move the ball with relative ease. A comparison of the statistics at the end of the first half gave the edge to Kansas City.

Disgruntled by their inability to perform as they had during the season, many of the Packers trailed into the locker room with their chins to their chests. Lombardi was waiting for them.

No one recorded precisely what the coach said in those tense moments between halves, but he was very hot. He chewed out the defense for playing too cautiously. "You're grabbing, not tackling," he bellowed. He ordered them to start blitzing.

In a corner of the locker room, Bart and Zeke Bratkowski huddled with the offensive coaches. "We'll just stick with the game plan," one of the coaches said.

"We know now that we were right, that they're weak at the corners. We'll keep hitting them there."

Early in the third quarter, the Chiefs had the ball on their own 49-yard line. It was third down and 5. Lenny Dawson dropped back to pass. The Packers blitzed. Dawson had to rush, and the ball was off target. Green Bay safetyman Willie Wood cut in front of the Chiefs' receiver to make the interception, and he streaked to the Kansas City 5. On the next play, Bart handed off to Elijah Pitts, who scored easily. Now it was 21–10, Green Bay.

If there still were doubts in anyone's mind about the final outcome, Bart surely settled them the next time Green Bay got the ball. He launched a 56-yard touchdown drive, tearing the Chiefs' defenses to ribbons with his deadly passing.

Three times he connected with Max McGee—once for 11 yards, once for 16 yards, and once for 13 yards, the play on which the touchdown was scored. In each case, the Kansas City cornerback was the victim.

Not long after the Green Bay touchdown, Willie Mitchell of the Chiefs intercepted one of Bart's passes. But the Kansas City offense sputtered and died, and they had to punt.

Starr came back in. As if to show them that Mitchell's interception had been a fluke, he sent Carroll Dale into Mitchell's zone on a deep square-out pattern. Dale brought down the ball for a 25-yard gain.

Moments later Bart threw into Mitchell's area again, this time with Max McGee the receiver. The play got Green Bay 37 yards. Five plays later Pitts ran the ball in. The scoreboard now read: Green Bay, 35; Kansas City, 10.

There were seven minutes remaining, but the Chiefs were a thoroughly beaten team. Lombardi, in an effort to stop the carnage, took Starr out. It ended, 35–10, with the Chiefs losers.

13

Super Starr

IN HIS FIRST DECADE with the Packers, Bart's name was seldom mentioned when anyone ticked off the great quarterbacks of the day. Sonny Jurgensen of the Redskins was regarded as a superior passer. Fran Tarkenton of the Vikings, and later the Giants, was considered a better runner. The Browns' Frank Ryan was called pro football's preeminent play caller.

As for quarterbacks of the future, no one was supposed to have the promise of either John Brodie of the 49ers or Don Meredith of the Cowboys.

And there was Johnny Unitas. During the late 1950's and most of the 1960's, every quarterback who laced on a cleat operated in the shadow of the great Johnny U.

But Bart's performance through the season of 1966,

in the NFL title game against the Cowboys and in the Super Bowl contest that followed, changed all that. At last, Starr began to receive the recognition he had deserved for so long.

Immediately after the Super Bowl, the writers balloted and named Bart the game's Most Valuable Player. Then *Sport* magazine presented him with the keys to a shiny new Corvette.

When Len Dawson heard the news, he allowed himself a gentle smile. "He was great," said Dawson. "He was truly a great quarterback. He took advantage of all the tools at his command."

The statistics of the game confirm this. Bart completed sixteen of twenty-three passes for 250 yards and two touchdowns.

But statistics tell only part of the story. Starr established his preeminence that warm afternoon in Los Angeles by his ability to deliver whenever he had to—on third down, in "must" situations.

Bart was faced with fifteen third-down plays to call. Incredibly, he made the first down twelve times. (By contrast, Dawson had eleven third-down plays. He failed on seven of them.) More than anything else, this is what destroyed Kansas City.

Kansas City coach Hank Stram paid tribute to Starr for his ability to deliver under pressure. In the locker room after, Stram said, "The thing that kept Green Bay going all day was Starr's ability—it was uncanny —to come up with the successful third-down play. Starr was the single biggest difference between the two teams."

Cornerback Fred Williamson, wearing a towel and a deep frown, came by. Williamson's boner in the second quarter resulted in a 64-yard touchdown pass that was canceled out by a penalty.

"It was third and one," said Williamson. "It was a running situation. He gambled on a pass, and the way he faked a run was tremendous. It sure fooled me."

Jerry Mays, a Kansas City defensive end, was another Starr booster. "We rushed hell out of him all day," Mays said. "But he just stood there and threw the ball."

Even before the Super Bowl, the praise for Bart was beginning to ring out.

No longer were the Packers regarded as purely a product of Coach Lombardi's genius. And no more were they said to rely primarily upon the strong bodies of Paul Hornung and Jim Taylor. Now they were a quarterback's club.

Passing had replaced running as Green Bay's prime weapon. In 1966, the Pack had rushed the ball for 1,673 yards and 98 first downs. But they had thrown the ball for 2,602 yards and 115 first downs. As Jimmy Cannon expressed it, "The age of muscle has ended at Green Bay."

This thought must have occurred to many of the game's observers, for late in the 1966 season Bart was announced as the landslide winner of the NFL's Most Valuable Player balloting.

Bart was acclaimed for his knowledge of pro defenses. "He has instant recall," declared Packer cornerback Herb Adderley, one of the NFL's most thoughtful students of quarterbacks.

"Once Bart sees a defense, he *knows* what every man is going to do the next time he sees it," Adderley declared. "This is an incredible ability. Some people call it smart signal calling. Actually, it's defense recognition. It explains Green Bay's success."

Any number of people agreed with Adderley. "You can't take any kind of a gamble against Starr," said Dick Voris, defensive coach of the 49ers. "Any gamble produces a weakness, and he always finds it. For instance, if you blitz him, he'll let you come within inches and then flick the ball out on a screen for a big gain."

George J. Halas, a scout for the Chicago Bears and a nephew of the legendary George S. Halas, had this comment about Bart: "I used to think that Johnny Unitas was the greatest quarterback in pro football. But now it would have to be Starr. He has proved it over a long time, Sunday after Sunday."

Comparing Starr's skills with those of Unitas isn't quite reasonable, however. As even the most casual observer of pro football realizes, they are different types.

Jimmy Orr, the Colts' veteran receiver, once put it this way: "Comparing Unitas and Starr is like comparing cheese and chalk. Johnny has freer control of the club. I think Bart follows a fairly strict game plan. But he is a brilliant play caller.

"Johnny gambles more. We're more of a gambling team. When we're in trouble, John usually throws.

When Green Bay is in trouble, Starr can do anything—run or throw or call a draw play that surprises the defenses."

Unitas is among the first to admit that he and Starr are different types. "Bart's an excellent quarterback," Johnny once told *Sports Illustrated*, "but he calls plays to control the ball. I gamble. I throw anytime."

But by 1966 it was no longer valid to characterize Starr as a quarterback who liked to play it safe. The NFL championship between the Packers and Cowboys that year is a case in point.

After the Cowboys had tied the game, 14–14, Bart got the Pack in front again with a 51-yard bomb to Carroll Dale. And in the closing minutes of the game, with the Packers only 7 points ahead, Bart didn't hesitate to put the ball in the air, and time and time again his passes clicked.

Curt Gowdy who was telecasting the game for NBC was wide-eyed. "Starr's reputation as a conservative quarterback goes out the window right now," he told his network audience.

Both Starr and Unitas came into the National League in 1956. Unitas was the No. 1 quarterback in Baltimore in 1957. It took Bart three years to achieve that status.

A comparison of statistics through the years leads to a number of conclusions about the pair. First of all, Unitas is more inclined to pass than Starr (through 1969, Unitas put the ball in the air more times than Starr), a fact that should not surprise anyone.

Bart is more accurate than Unitas. Through 1969,

Bart ranked as pro football's most accurate passer of all time, with 1,644 completions in 2,849 attempts, a 58.8 completion percentage.

Unitas, however, is more likely to throw the bomb, to pass for long yardage. Through 1969, Unitas had 266 touchdown passes, highest total in league history. No other active passer was close to that figure. Bart had 144.

Even though Bart throws shorter passes than Unitas, he and the Colt star show almost the same figure for the average gain per attempt. Why? One expert says that because Starr throws less often, his receivers are usually not covered closely. When one gets the ball, he often has ample running room.

Tex Maule of *Sports Illustrated* summed up the Starr-Unitas debate the best. Said Maule: "As everyone knows, Unitas is one of the finest quarterbacks of all time. As everyone *should* know, Starr is one of them, too."

14

"I'm Still Learning"

As THEY ASSEMBLED at training camp at St. Norbert's College in West De Pere, Wisconsin, in the summer of 1967, the Packers had one glittering objective—to win their third straight National Football League championship, a feat never accomplished in the game's history.

In 1967, the Eastern and Western conferences of the National Football League were split into two four-team divisions—the Central and Coastal divisions. Green Bay was a team in the Central Division, which also included Chicago, Detroit, and Minnesota. Each team was to play home-and-home games with each member of its division, plus single games with teams in other divisions.

Preseason prognosticators judged the Packers to be

the class of their division. "The Packers just get better," said *Sports Illustrated*. "They can win pretty much as they please."

Although Hornung and Taylor were no longer with the team, skilled replacements had been found in Elijah Pitts, one of the team's stalwarts in 1966, and Donny Anderson and Jim Grabowski, rookies the previous season but now ready for full-time duty.

Experts noted, however, that the offensive line was aging, that tackles Bob Skoronski and Forrest Gregg and guards Fuzzy Thurston and Jerry Kramer were more than thirty. Yet they seemed to be aging gracefully. If they had slowed down, nobody had noticed it.

The Green Bay defense was rated as the best in the business. No other team could boast linebackers to equal Dave Robinson, Lee Roy Caffey, and Ray Nitschke in speed and cunning. And in 1966 Willie Davis had won All-Pro honors at end, and Henry Jordan at defensive tackle.

During 1966 the Packers had held the opposition to 7 points or less six times and had given up an average of 11.6 points per game, the lowest figure in the league.

Despite the Packers' hopefulness, it was not a sunny year. Things began to go wrong in training season when Bart was struck with a number of injuries. They piled one atop the other—a pulled hamstring, a jammed thumb, and torn leg muscles. Bart spent much of the exhibition season on the sidelines, not running, not throwing, not doing anything.

The Packers opened 1967 with a tie against the Lions, not rated as one of the league's powerhouse teams. The next week in Green Bay they beat the Bears, but just barely. The score was 13–10.

It was a long and trying afternoon for Bart. He was intercepted five times. *Five times!* In *all* of 1966 Bart had been intercepted only three times.

Rosey Taylor, a defensive back for the Bears, observed that Bart wasn't throwing the ball with his usual zip. "He wasn't snapping his wrist when he followed through," Taylor said. "The ball didn't have its usual zing."

But Vince Lombardi denied that his quarterback was below par. "We're just having a helluva time," the coach said.

"Maybe we're pressing. We're not loose. We're not playing with the abandon that used to characterize our play."

After the game, the green-carpeted Packer locker room was strangely quiet, almost as if the team had lost.

A reporter watched Bart, tired and low in spirits, go through a bizarre postgame ceremony, one that was to become a weekly ritual.

Bart started by removing his conventional protective armor—the shoulder pads, rib pads, hip pads, thigh guards, and all the rest.

He then stripped off the tape that covered painfully bruised ribs, an injury he had suffered in an exhibition game. Beneath the tape, Bart wore a tough hard-plastic pad backed with soft padding.

Next, Bart ripped off a length of tape from the

thumb of his passing hand. The thumb had sustained a sprain during a scrimmage.

Last, Bart unwound a long cotton leg wrap, rolling it into a tight spiral.

"Bart," the reporter said, "I've never seen you so beat up."

Bart, now sitting on a bench, took a swig from a soft drink. "I'd rather not talk about injuries," he said softly. "I just don't want to make a big thing out of them."

His wish notwithstanding, it must be said that during 1967 Bart's injuries were a "big thing," a very big thing.

The next week against the Atlanta Falcons the situation got worse. In the first quarter, Bart dropped back to pass in the face of a Falcon blitz. Bob Riggle, the Atlanta safety, slammed into Bart first. Right behind came Tommy Nobis, the Falcons' 6-foot 2-inch, 235-pound linebacker. The two combined to upend Bart and fling him to the ground like a toy doll. When Bart managed to get to his feet, he found that his right arm had gone dead, the result of a pinched nerve.

Bart saw the rest of the game from the bench. Zeke Bratkowski took over and led the team to a 23–0 win.

Lombardi again attempted to deny the fact that Bart was injured. "He's just in a slump, like a batter in baseball," the coach told reporters. "It happens to everyone sooner or later."

But after the Atlanta game, Lombardi could not hide the facts any longer. "Starr has been playing under a severe handicap all year," the coach announced on his television program in Green Bay one evening. "I've denied the fact he was injured," the coach admitted, "but I've done it in order to protect him, not from the fans or newspapers, but from the opposition."

To Bart, the injuries and the pain were not the worst of it. There were the poor performances, the interceptions, a total of nine of them after the Atlanta game.

That was not all. The first time Bart appeared on the field at Milwaukee Stadium for the game against the Falcons, he was greeted with boos. There were cheers, too, but the boos made a vivid impression. Little wonder that there were times that season that Bart, to quote him, "was ready to give it up."

After the game with the Falcons, Bratkowski quarterbacked the team for the next two weeks. The Packers downed the Lions but were beaten by the Vikings.

Rumors were now beginning to circulate that something was wrong with the mighty Packers, that they were ready to be taken. The team was getting old, it was said, and age was causing key men to slow down. Bart was supposed to be only a shadow of his former self.

The day before the Packers were to play the Giants in New York, Lombardi announced that Starr was well and would start. The news buoyed the team. "Bart is our quarterback," said tackle Forrest Gregg. "With Bart back, we get a lift."

On Green Bay's first play from scrimmage, Bart threw deep to Carroll Dale. Dale was open, but the ball dropped by several feet. It looked as if it was going to be another troublesome afternoon for the Packers. They were behind, 14–10, at the half.

Then Bart began to click. Relying mainly on sweeps, he led a 63-yard touchdown drive early in the third quarter and broke the game open with his passes in the fourth period when the Packers scored four times, once on a 38-yard pass from Bart to Jim Grabowski. It was Bart's first touchdown pass of the season.

It was a day everything seemed to work. The final score saw the Packers on top, 48–21. Not only was the game an important victory, but it laid to rest the rumors about the team's old age and Starr's lack of effectiveness.

With Bart doing the quarterbacking, the Packers went on to win three of their next four games, but it was very late in the season before Bart was in good health again. He had a brilliant afternoon against the Chicago Bears on the last Sunday in November, as the Packers clinched the Central Division title.

Bart saved one of his best performances for the Western Conference play-off game. The Packers faced the Los Angeles Rams. Bart hit with seventeen out of twenty-two passes for 222 yards and one touchdown. He mixed in running plays beautifully, often going to speedy Travis Williams on quick openers. The Packers won, 28–7.

Then came the epic battle with Dallas for the NFL championship. The game started out well for the Packers, then turned. In the early stages Bart had twice hit Boyd Dowler with touchdown passes and earned a

14–0 lead. But the Dallas defense became wise and began to pick up the Green Bay wide receivers or storm in.

On one blitz Bart fumbled, and the Cowboys turned it into a touchdown. Another Packer fumble gave Dallas field position for a field goal. That made it 14–10. It became 17–14, Dallas, on a razzle-dazzle lateral-forward pass play that went from quarterback Don Meredith to Lance Rentzel.

Now the stage was set for Bart's last-ditch heroics (described in Chapter 1)—the 68-yard touchdown march in the game's dying minutes, then the bold sneak into the end zone behind Jerry Kramer's block for the game-winning touchdown.

In the dressing room after, the biggest crush of newsmen surrounded Bart's dressing stall. One repor-ter asked, "What was the key play in the last drive?"

Bart thought a moment, then said, "There were two, actually—the pass to Mercein for nineteen yards that put the ball on the Dallas eleven-yard line was one of them. And Mercein's eight-yard run on the next play that got us down to the three was the other."

"You mean the play where you suckered out Lilly?" the reporter asked.

The smile on Bart's face suddenly dissolved. "I would rather not use the word 'suckered,' " he said, "certainly not when talking about Lilly. He's so fast and he reacts so quickly, he just had to go with Gillingham."

Two weeks later, the Packers met the Oakland

Raiders, the American League champions, in the Super Bowl. The Raiders had completed the season with a 13–1 record, the best in pro football. Many people felt they were better prepared to stop the Packers than the Kansas City Chiefs had been the year before.

Oakland's quarterback, Daryle Lamonica, had been made Player of the Year in the AFL, and six other members of the team had won All-Pro honors. George Blanda, who led the AFL in scoring with twenty field goals and fifty-six out of fifty-seven conversions, had been another major reason for Oakland's success. Some experts said that Blanda's kicking skill could spell the difference if the game was close.

The Packers, on the other hand, were said to be not quite as strong as they had been the year before. They were bringing a 9-4-1 record into the game, compared to a 12-2 record in 1967. Two Green Bay stars, Elijah Pitts and Jim Grabowski, would not play because of injuries.

The Oakland team resembled Green Bay in a number of ways. They put a great stress on defense. And the Raiders' offense contained many of the basics long attributed to the Packers—a solid running game, both a long and short passing attack, and well-drilled units of kickoff and kick-return specialists.

While the teams were rated similar in many respects, one sharp difference loomed—at quarterback. Bart Starr, completing his twelfth year in professional football, had often been subjected to the pressures of championship play. Tall, strong Daryle Lamonica had not been. Indeed, he had been a starting quarterback for only one season, having served as backup man to Jack Kemp at Buffalo for four years. This difference was to prove significant.

One other factor must be mentioned. Rumors were being circulated that this was to be Vince Lombardi's last year as Green Bay's coach. He was evasive about his future plans, saying only that, "I'll be in Green Bay next year." But as the Packers' coach? He wouldn't say.

Miami's Orange Bowl was the game's site. The stakes, aside from the prestige of the championship, were again of super size—$15,000 for each winning player, and $7,500 for each loser.

The Oakland defense proved troublesome—at first. Bart moved his plays around, trying to find the weak spots.

The first quarter ended with Green Bay ahead, 3–0, on the strength of a field goal by Don Chandler. Yet the closeness of the score in no way reflected the Packers' outlook. Starr and his teammates were brimming with confidence.

Early in the second quarter, a fine Oakland punt buried Green Bay deep in their own territory. Slowly, methodically, Bart steered the team from the Green Bay 3-yard line to the Oakland 36. It was fourth down with 1 yard to go. Bart, showing his assurance, disdaining a punt, called a running play. Even if it had failed, the boldness of the call was enough to unnerve the Raiders. As it was, the play gained 5 yards, more than enough for a first down.

Soon after, Chandler booted the Packers' second field goal to put them ahead, 6–0.

"Never leave the door open for the Packers," rival coaches often say. "They'll walk right through." The Packers' first touchdown demonstrated the truth of this precept.

Bart had noticed that the Oakland cornerbacks were playing extremely tight on the Green Bay receivers, much tighter than was usual in the National League. To take advantage of this tendency, Bart called a deep pass. As he drifted back to throw, Bart saw Boyd Dowler head downfield, and Kent McCloughan, the Oakland cornerback, move to cover him. But Dowler simply bulled his way past McCloughan, then veered toward the middle and into the clear. Bart threw a strike. Dowler caught the ball on the Oakland 40-yard line and went the rest of the way without anyone touching him. Chandler's extra point boot gave Green Bay a 13-point lead.

It was then the Raiders' turn to cause some fireworks. Within the next two minutes they drove 78 yards to a touchdown in nine plays.

In the closing seconds of the second quarter, Bart hit Dowler with a short sideline pass to set up another field goal. This made the score 16–7, and that's the way it stood when the Packers left the field at half time.

Many of those who saw the game say that Green Bay delivered the clincher early in the third quarter. The Packers had the ball on the Green Bay 40-yard line. It was third down and 1. The young Oakland line braced for a run.

Bart took the snap, faked beautifully to his fullback who blasted into the line, and then scampered back, his arm cocked to throw. The Raider defense was caught completely off guard, and it was easy for Bart to hit Max McGee, who promptly turned the pass into a 35-yard gain.

The starch seemed to come out of the Raiders after that. Bart then hit Donny Anderson and Carroll Dale on short passes that put the ball on the Oakland 1. Anderson scored from there.

In the final period Herb Adderley intercepted one of Lamonica's passes and streaked 60 yards for another touchdown. This killed any remaining hope the Raiders might have had.

Midway in the fourth quarter, Bart suffered a jammed right thumb and had to leave the game. He watched from the sidelines as Bratkowski mopped up. The final score: Green Bay, 33; Oakland, 14.

All in all, the game was a typical Bart Starr performance.

He worked with his usual devastating efficiency in picking apart the Oakland defenses. He ran his ball carriers with perfection. He threw with unfailing accuracy on his short passes. And when he needed the bomb—the long pass—he reached into his bulging bag of tricks and came up with it.

Bart summed up his performance in typically modest fashion: "You reach here. You reach there. You probe, pick, and pass, and you see what you can get."

The sportswriters who attended the game had a more enthusiastic view of what he had accomplished, and they voted him to be the game's Most Valuable Player. For the second consecutive year, Bart was awarded the Corvette sports car by *Sport* magazine.

When the game ended, an incident took place that few people noticed. Thousands of fans poured out onto the field, clapping the players on the back. Bart threaded his way through the melee to the Oakland side of the field.

Daryle Lamonica, his head down, was heading for the dressing room. He looked up when he saw Starr approaching.

Bart, smiling, put out his hand. Daryle took it. Then a grin crossed his face.

"Don't let it get you," Bart said. "It took me seven years to learn—and I'm still learning."

Then Bart Starr turned and headed for the Packer locker room.

15

Star-Crossed Season

"WHAT'S WRONG WITH the Packers?"

Bart was asked that question a hundred times during the 1968 season. Newspapermen, fans, and rival players wanted to know the answer. It was a question the Packers often asked themselves.

Granted, a team that has won three consecutive National Football League titles and two World (Super Bowl) Championships is operating in the stratosphere. Down is virtually the only direction in which it can go.

Yet the Packers did more than merely stumble. They crumbled; they collapsed.

How could a team with the Packers' great poise and dedication, the scourge of professional football, suffer a season in which they lost more games than they won?

What *did* go wrong?

The answer is complex.

The story of the cheerless season begins in Green
Bay on a frigid February night. The scene is the
Oneida Country Club. Vince Lombardi, facing a doz-
en microphones and television and film cameras, announces he is retiring as a coach, but that he will
remain as general manager of the Packers.

The announcement is brief but emotional. It is obvi-
ously a decision that Lombardi has weighed carefully.
He explains that being both coach *and* general manager "is too much responsibility for one man."

Before leaving the microphones, Lombardi says,
"Gentlemen, let me introduce you to the new football
coach of the Green Bay Packers, Phil Bengston."

Phil Bengston?

While Phil Bengston was scarcely a household
name, he was well known to the Packer players and
fans. A tall, slight man, retiring and quiet, Bengston
had been Green Bay's defensive coach since 1959.

Bengston, fifty-four at the time, had been an All-
American tackle at the University of Minnesota. He
had served as an assistant coach at the University
of Missouri and Stanford University. Before joining
the Packers, he had been a coaching assistant with the
49ers.

Bart knew Bengston to be, like Lombardi, a perfec-
tionist, dedicated and thorough.

The team was going to miss Vince Lombardi's
coaching skills and his ability to arouse the players.
Nobody doubted that. But would it make any difference in the way the team performed? That was the
question.

The players were optimistic as the season drew near. And they had good reason to be. Running backs Jim Grabowski and Elijah Pitts would be back in the lineup, and Donny Anderson and Travis Williams each would be carrying another year of experience. The receivers—Boyd Dowler, Carroll Dale, and Marv Fleming—were the same trio who had performed so capably the year before.

There were to be no changes in the defensive line and none in the linebacking corps. Tackle Francis Peay, obtained from the Giants in an off-season trade, was expected to strengthen the offensive line.

Starr was in excellent health. So was Bratkowski.

Lombardi, on the night he retired as coach, had said, "The greatness of the Packers is ahead of them." The players were in full agreement.

The opening of training camp was delayed a few days because of labor problems. The league's players, dissatisfied with pension proposals made by the owners, went on strike. The owners then closed down training facilities.

Bart knew a delay would be harmful, so he and Jim Weatherwax got the veteran Packer players together for workouts at a high school field. They worked the players as hard as Lombardi ever did.

When training camp did open, it was not the same. Some of the players did not try quite so hard. Regulations were not as strict or as strictly observed.

"Some guys definitely took advantage of Phil," Jerry Kramer disclosed in *Farewell to Football*. "Guys would sneak over in the shade sometimes and lie on the ground. Nobody ever took a breather when Vince was around."

The team lost two exhibition games, but nobody seemed very much concerned. The Packers had lost two in 1966, a season they won the NFL title and the Super Bowl.

One thing was obvious to the players at this stage. Bengston was no motivator. He did not excite the players or stimulate them.

"Motivation is going to have to come more from the players themselves than it did in the past," said one Packer veteran. "We are going to have to function more on individual pride."

Most of the team members remained confident. Even if there were any growing doubts, they were surely dispelled with the Packers' easy win over the Philadelphia Eagles in the first game of the season. Bart was in fine form, passing to Dale and Dowler for touchdowns in leading the 30–13 rout.

But the next week gave a taste of what was to come. The Packers faced the Vikings. Minnesota scored early in the game after intercepting one of Bart's passes. They led at half time, 16–0, and won, 26–13. The next week the Packers lost again, this time to the Lions. Bart was intercepted three times.

Bart was disappointed, disappointed in himself. He was fond of Bengston. He felt he was letting him down.

The Packers bounced back against Atlanta the next

week, but Bart was injured. He thought he would be well enough to play against Los Angeles the following Sunday, but while he was throwing in a pregame warm-up, he felt something "pop" in his arm. He had pulled a muscle. He spent the day on the bench.

Bratkowski was intercepted three times and fumbled once, and the Packers lost another. A field goal with fifty-five seconds to go beat them, 16–14.

Now the question began to be heard: "What's wrong with the Packers?"

One thing wrong was injuries. Starr was only one of the walking wounded.

Bill Brown, a defensive lineman, broke his arm during training season. Later he broke his leg. Henry Jordan, the team's All-Pro tackle, was in agony with a bad back. Jim Weatherwax, also a tackle, tore a cartilage and required surgery. He was out for the season. Ron Kostelnik, still another tackle, had knee problems, too.

Jordan and Kostelnik continued to play, but the team did not have its usual defensive strength through the middle.

Another answer to the question "What's wrong with the Packers?" had to do with the place-kicking situation. Jerry Kramer had been the kicker early in the season. But when he injured his knee, Bengston turned to Chuck Mercein.

When Mercein proved ineffective, Bengston switched to Errol Mann. Mann missed twice against the Bears. Then Bengston went back to Mercein. He finally settled upon Mike Mercer, a free agent. A few extra field goals in the right places could have turned at least two or three of the Packers' defeats into victories.

Detroit was next on the Green Bay schedule. Bart was not supposed to play. However, late in the game, Bratkowski was hit hard and stunned.

As his teammates helped Bratkowski from the field, Bengston turned to Bart. "Can you go in?" he asked.

Bart nodded, grabbed his helmet, and ran out on the field.

The Lions, ahead by a 14–7 score, exchanged knowing glances as the Packers huddled. They knew that Bart's arm was hurting, that he could not throw. So, anticipating a run, they closed up their defense.

Bart crossed them up. Ignoring the fierce pain, he threw to Boyd Dowler in the end zone. No one was near Dowler when he grabbed the ball. Chuck Mercein booted the extra point and the game was deadlocked. It ended, still tied, moments later.

The Packers now had a season record of 2-3-1. It was obvious that they were going nowhere. Their up-coming game was against the Dallas Cowboys, the only undefeated team in professional football at the time.

The game was played before 74,460 fans at the Cotton Bowl and a huge national television audience. Bart rose to the occasion.

The Packers were down, 10–7, at the half, but Bart rallied the team in the third quarter, connecting on touchdown passes of 3 and 32 yards to Marv Fleming.

Then Bart hit Boyd Dowler with a 5-yard touchdown throw in the final period to clinch the game.

It was like old times. There was great joy in the Green Bay locker room after the game. The team was rolling.

"It's downhill from now on," said one player. "All we have to do is beat Chicago next week and Minnesota the week after, and we'll knock them both out of contention."

"Right!" another player chimed in. "And Detroit figures to lose its games to the Rams and the Colts those two weeks."

The first player grinned and nodded. "We'll be in first place and have clear sailing."

It did not work out that way.

The Packers lost to the Bears, but on a fluke, on a rare free-kick play. In professional football a team is allowed a free field-goal kick after a fair catch of an opponent's punt. With twenty seconds remaining in the game, the Bears invoked this rule.

Mac Percival did the kicking for the Bears. The Green Bay linemen were not permitted to rush. The kick traveled 43 yards and was good, providing the margin of victory in the Bears' 13–10 win.

The Packers lost to the Vikings, too. The score was 14–10. Three times the Packers handed the ball away on fumbles.

After Green Bay's loss to Minnesota, the standings —won, lost, and tied—in the Central Division looked like this:

Chicago	5	4	0
Minnesota	5	4	0
Detroit	3	5	1
Green Bay	3	5	1

A close observer would not have to look at the standings to know that the Packers were sharing last place. When a team is performing poorly, the players often become embittered. There are squabbles. There is dissension. The Packers of 1968 suffered these miseries.

Bart, as the team's veteran leader, decided it was his responsibility to do something about the situation. A party, that would do the trick, he figured. Bring the team together in an informal meeting. Surely that would help restore the Packers' sparkle and confidence.

At first Bart planned to have the party at his home. But the players convinced him it would be too much work for his wife.

"Let's have it at the bowling alley," someone suggested. Bart agreed. So on a cold November night, the Green Bay team gathered together at the Century Bowling Alley in West De Pere, Wisconsin, a few miles from Green Bay, the guests of Mr. and Mrs. Bart Starr.

The party, as described by Jerry Kramer in *Farewell to Football,* got off to a poor start and then went downhill. For reasons that are obscure, end Marv Fleming began quarreling with big offensive tackle Francis Peay. Peay burst into anger and threw his Coke in Fleming's face.

"The whole party went poof," Kramer said.

Despite the strife and the sagging morale, the Packers managed to win their next two games, beating New Orleans and Washington. Bart's injuries kept him on the bench for the game against the Redskins, but Bratkowski was in top form, hitting on eighteen out of twenty-four passes in steering the Packers to a 27–7 victory.

The two wins gave the Packers a .500 record again and put them right back in the race for the division crown. With three games remaining, the standings looked like this:

Minnesota	6	5	0
Green Bay	5	5	1
Chicago	5	6	0
Detroit	3	6	2

The 49ers were next on Green Bay's schedule. Before the game, Lombardi spoke to the team, the first time he had done so all season. He talked of Green Bay's past triumphs when the chips were down, of the team's days of glory. The Lombardi magic worked. When the Packers raced out onto the field, they were soaring.

The Green Bay game plan called for the team to run the ball constantly. They knew they had to do this to keep the 49ers' pass rushers honest. Otherwise, they would blitz and red-dog, and Bengston knew that Starr's aching ribs could not stand such treatment.

"One good blow and Bart is out of there," Bengston told the offensive line before the game.

For a time the Green Bay strategy worked to perfection. After the Packers received the opening kickoff, Bart directed an 80-yard touchdown march, handing off to Jim Grabowski, who leaped into the end zone for the final yard. Only once during the drive did Bart pass, and that was a quick 5 yarder.

Dick Nolan, the 49er coach, caught on to what was happening, and he then adjusted his team's defense to stifle the Green Bay ground attack.

Bart then had no choice but to go to the air. Mixing passes and runs, he managed to get the team deep enough into San Francisco territory to allow Mike Mercer to boot a field goal.

But Bart paid a heavy price. Tackles Charlie Kruger and Roland Lakes and linebacker Matt Hazeltine slammed Bart to the ground on three of the five pass plays he tried. The last time he hit the ground, Bart's side came ablaze with pain. He knew he was through for the day.

Bratkowski came in and performed with his usual neat-handed skill. But early in the quarter, the San Francisco blitzers racked up Bratkowski. To replace him, Bengston sent in Billy Stevens, a rookie from the University of Texas at El Paso. Stevens had never appeared in a professional game before, and his lack of experience was conspicuous.

Bart, a warm-up jacket about his shoulders, watched from the sidelines, and what he saw made him writhe.

Young Stevens was unable to move the team. When he went back to pass, the 49ers stormed in and trampled him into the ground.

Time after time, Green Bay was forced to punt. Donny Anderson had to kick into the wind and the punts were short.

The 49ers scored 20 points in that quarter, and they whipped the Packers, 27–20. Never before in his thirteen years with the team had Bart seen the Packers so inept. And he was powerless to do anything. That made it worse.

The Packer locker room after the game was a dismal scene. There were some wet eyes.

Lombardi was there. His face was ashen.

Reporters milled about Starr. He dodged questions about his ribs. "I'd rather not say anything. It might sound like an alibi."

There was hardly a word spoken on the plane trip back to Green Bay. Bart did a lot of thinking. In all his experience, he could not recall a season so terribly agonizing. He remembered the team's defeat at the hands of the Philadelphia Eagles in the 1960 championship game. He recalled the grim afternoon at Yankee Stadium in 1959 when Lombardi had kept him on the bench in favor of Joe Francis. But this was worse, much worse.

Mathematically, the Packers still had a chance. But they lost to the Colts the next week, 16–3, and were virtually eliminated from the 1968 championship race. The next day Chicago beat Los Angeles, and Minnesota downed San Francisco, and the Packers were then mathematically out of it.

Bart was not in the lineup against the Colts. But he remembers the day clearly, and one scene in particular stands out in his mind.

The game was played in Lambeau Stadium on December 7. In observance of the date, the Packer management passed out small American flags to the 50, 861 fans who attended.

After the final gun sounded, as Bart and the other players were leaving the field for the long walk up the ramp to the locker room, the voice of the public address announcer suddenly rang out: "How about an ovation for the Packers? They've given us some great football over the years."

With that, every person in Lambeau Stadium stood. And they waved the small flags, and they cheered and cheered.

Bart felt miserable about the team's sorry season. His side had an agonizing ache. But the fans exhilarated him. It was an unforgettable moment. Bart had tears in his eyes when he reached the Packer locker room.

Except for one or two bright moments, the 1968 season is a bad dream. Bart is trying to forget it.

"What really hurt," says Bart, "is that we didn't play well for Coach Phil.

"We wanted to show we could and would win for him. And we didn't. That's what was sickening to us."

16
"The Pack Will Be Back"

THE THOUGHT OF RETIREMENT entered Bart's mind often during the late 1960's. He gave the idea very serious consideration during the winter of 1967–1968.

"When we came off our second Super Bowl triumph and we were on top of the world, I did think about giving up football," Bart admits.

"But after the disappointing season of 1968, my prime target became 1969 and coming back to play one more time."

The 1969 season marked Bart's fourteenth season in a Green Bay uniform. His is one of the longest careers in pro football history.

Bart has been able to achieve such longevity for several reasons. First of all, he played as quarterback, and the rules serve to protect the quarterback, at least in his role as a passer.

And Bart, through the great bulk of his career, had the good fortune to play behind tough, dedicated linemen. To players like Bob Skoronski, Fuzzy Thurston, Jerry Kramer, and Forrest Gregg, Starr's person was inviolable.

Bart also benefited from the fact that he stayed in top-notch physical condition, not smoking, not drinking.

History was in Bart's favor, too. Many of the game's great quarterbacks played well into their thirties. Y. A. Tittle and Charlie Conerly of the Giants, and Sammy Baugh of the Redskins, all were thirty-eight when they played their last season.

Quarterback Earl Morrall of the Colts won NFL Player of the Year honors at thirty-four. Johnny Unitas embarked upon a comeback at the age of thirty-six.

Bart was thirty-five when he began his fourteenth season.

Bart's health, up until the late 1960's, was consistently good. He did not suffer any serious injury until 1963, the year he broke his hand. That sidelined him for a month. Another injury kept him on the bench when the Packers met the Colts in the 1965 sudden-death play-off game.

During the 1967 season, Bart was often in pitiable condition, with his rib cage, a shoulder, and a hand all hurting. The year 1968 was even worse. Bart did not play much more than half the time.

But when the 1969 exhibition season opened, Bart felt like his old self. And, in spite of the team's poor showing the year before, an aura of optimism prevailed.

"The Pack Will Be Back!" had become Green Bay's rallying cry. It was blazoned on restaurant menus and store-window placards. Seemingly, every automobile in the state of Wisconsin displayed a bumper sticker that proclaimed the battle cry.

"We'll Win with Bengston!" and "Green Bay's Fine in '69!" were other slogans coined to help rejuvenate the team.

When the Packers turned out for training camp, they found a new Coach Bengston. He was much more demanding than he had been the season before, displaying a Lombardi-like toughness.

Bengston unveiled a new weapon—aerobics. He defined it as a scientific means of increasing the amount of available oxygen in the system.

The Packer players defined it as hard work. Each man was required to be able to run a torturous series of wind sprints—as many as ten consecutive 100-yard dashes with one-minute rests in between.

The idea was for each player to achieve a new level of stamina and endurance. "What we're after," explained Zeke Bratkowski, who had become an assistant coach, "is the ability to run full bore, come back to the huddle, and twenty seconds later be able to run full bore again."

There were several new faces in the Packer lineup for 1969, but there was plenty of experience, too. No less than five players had ten or more years of service in professional football.

Boyd Dowler was beginning his eleventh season; Ray Nitschke and Willie Davis were each beginning their twelfth, and Henry Jordan was starting his thirteenth. Bart, of course, ranked as the veteran of veterans.

Despite the hard work and an improved attitude on the part of the players, the 1969 season was almost a replay of the previous year for the Packers. Again Bart was often sidelined with painful injuries. The Packers finished in third place in the Central Division for the second consecutive year.

Vince Lombardi now coaches the Washington Redskins. Yet many of his precepts still guide Bart.

One is uppermost in Bart's mind. "The greatest achievement," Lombardi used to tell the team, "is not in never falling, but in rising after you fall."

The Packers fell. But Bart believes they will rise, that they will be champions again. And more than anything else, Bart wants to be the one who leads them back.

Bart Starr
Lifetime Statistics

Season Records

Year	At-tempts	Com-pleted	Yards	TD's	Inter-cep-tions	Aver-age	Per-cent
1956	44	24	325	2	3	7.49	54.5
1957	215	117	1,489	3	10	6.93	54.4
1958	157	78	875	3	12	5.57	49.7
1959	134	70	972	6	7	7.25	52.2
1960	172	98	1,358	4	8	7.90	57.0
1961	295	172	2,418	16	16	8.19	58.3
1962	285	178	2,438	12	9	8.55	62.5
1963	244	132	1,855	15	10	7.60	54.1
1964	272	163	2,144	15	4	7.88	59.9
1965	251	140	2,055	16	9	8.19	55.8
1966	251	156	2,257	14	3	8.99	62.2
1967	210	115	1,823	9	17	8.68	54.8
1968	171	109	1,617	15	8	9.46	63.7
1969	148	92	1,161	9	6	7.84	62.2

NFL Championship Games

Year	Attempts	Com-pleted	Yards	TD's	Inter-ceptions	Per-cents
1960	35	21	178	1	0	60.0
1961	17	10	164	3	0	58.8
1962	22	10	106	0	0	45.5
1965	19	10	147	1	1	52.6
1966	28	19	304	4	0	67.9
1967	24	14	191	2	0	58.3

World Championship (Super Bowl) Games

Year	Attempts	Com-pleted	Yards	TD's	Inter-ceptions	Per-cents
1967	23	16	250	2	1	69.6
1968	24	13	202	1	0	54.1

Index

Adderly, Herb, 156, 169
Alabama, University of, 13, 28–29
American Football League, 139 ff.
Anderson, Bill, 108
Anderson, Donny, 131, 160, 169, 173, 181
Atlanta Falcons, 17–18, 162–63

Baltimore Colts, 46, 53, 56–58, 74–75, 81, 102-3, 107–11, 181–82
Barnes, Erich, 95
Baugh, Sammy, 184
Baughan, Maxie, 64
Bednarik, Chuck, 60, 63, 90
Bengston, Phil, 172 ff.
Blackbourn, Lisle, 41, 44–45
Blaik, Earl, 72
Blanda, George, 166
Bratkowski, Zeke, 18, 109–11, 150, 162, 169, 175, 179–80, 185
Bread-and-butter play, 129
Brodie, John, 153
Brown, Bill, 175
Brown, Jimmy, 111–12
Brown, Roger, 18, 91
Brown, Tom, 144
Bryant, Bear, 28
Buchanan, Buck, 147–48
Burroughs, Dan, 64

Caffey, Lee Roy, 143, 160
Cannon, Jimmy, 155
Casares, Rick, 55
Cassady, Howard, 34
Chandler, Don, 16, 35, 95, 103, 111–12, 143, 148, 167–68
Chicago Bears, 51, 54–55, 57–58, 74, 80, 98, 100–1, 106–7, 164, 177, 179
Christiansen, Jack, 21
Clarke, Frank, 143
Cleveland Browns, 16–17, 80, 101–2, 111–13
Collier, Jim, 95
Conerly, Charlie, 82, 184

Crowley, Jim, 71
Cuozzo, Gary, 109
Currie, Dan, 94

Dale, Carroll, 10, 18, 105–6, 111–12, 117, 141, 149, 151, 157, 163, 169, 173
Dallas Cowboys, 9 ff., 140–45, 164–65, 176
Davis, Willie, 89, 160, 186
Dawson, Len, 146, 151, 154
Dean, Ted, 63
Dee, Johnny, 35
Detroit Lions, 18–19, 46, 51, 81, 90–92, 100–1, 104–6, 176, 179
Devaney, John, 43, 71
Dowler, Boyd, 16, 20, 53, 59, 61, 64, 68, 80, 86, 108, 129, 142, 164, 168, 173, 176–77, 186
Drew, Red, 31, 33–34

Farewell to Football (Kramer), 173–74, 178
Fears, Tom, 90
Fleming, Marv, 103, 142, 148, 150, 173, 176, 178
Forester, Bill, 61
Francis, Joe, 51, 53, 181

Galimore, Willie, 55
George, Bill, 80, 119
Gillingham, Gale, 10
Gilmer, Harry, 29, 32
Glass, Bill, 119–20
Gowdy, Curt, 157
Grabowski, Jim, 131, 141, 160, 164, 166, 173, 180
Green Bay Packers, 9 ff., 16 ff., 49 ff., 79 ff., 139 ff., 159 ff., 171 ff.
   history of club, 37 ff.
Green Bay *Press Gazette*, 60, 115
Gregg, Forrest, 79, 85, 160, 163, 184
Grier, Rosey, 82
Gremminger, Henry, 87
Gros, Earl, 98

188

Halas, George, 156
Hanner, Dave, 44
Hayes, Bob, 144
Hazeltine, Matt, 180
Hill, Jimmy, 99
Horner, Sam, 95
Hornung, Paul, 20, 44, 51, 54, 57–58, 61, 67, 69, 77, 80, 84–85, 89, 92 ff., 112, 131, 137, 155, 160
Howell, Jim Lee, 72
Howley, Chuck, 142
Huff, Sam, 20, 82, 85, 134
Hutson, Don, 40

Indian Packing Company, 38

Johnson, Jim, 104
Jordan, Henry, 73, 82, 160, 175, 186
Jurgensen, Sonny, 153

Kansas City Chiefs, 145 ff.
Karras, Alex, 91, 105
Katcavage, Jim, 82
Kemp, Jack, 167
King, Phil, 19, 94
Knalfelc, Gary, 59, 63–64
Kostelnik, Ron, 175
Kramer, Jerry, 11, 19, 53, 68, 75, 79, 85, 87–89, 91–92, 94–96, 103, 120, 160, 165, 173–75, 178–79, 184
Kruger, Charlie, 180

Lakes, Roland, 180
Lambeau, Curly, 38
Lamonica, Daryle, 165–70
Layne, Bobby, 43
Lilly, Bob, 10–11
Logan, Jerry, 102, 108
Lombardi, Vince, 49 ff., 69 ff., 83 ff., 103, 107, 125, 131 ff., 150, 152, 179, 181, 186
  early coaching career, 71–73
  resignation, 172
Long, Bob, 105
Lyles, Lenny, 108
Los Angeles Rams, 58–59, 81, 164

Mann, Errol, 175
Matte, Tom, 109
Maule, Tex, 158
Mays, Jerry, 155
McCloughan, Kent, 168

McDonald, Tommy, 61
McGee, Max, 17, 57, 59, 62–65, 68–69, 75, 79, 95, 99, 142, 147 ff., 169
McHan, Lamar, 51–52, 54–55, 70, 109
McLean, Ray, 45–46
McRae, Bennie, 98
Mercein, Chuck, 10, 165, 175
Mercer, Mike, 176, 180
Meredith, Don, 69, 143–45, 153, 165
Minnesota Vikings, 174, 177, 179
Mitchell, Willie, 149, 151
Modzelewski, Dick, 82
Montgomery, Alabama, 13, 25
Moore, Tom, 62–63, 75, 98, 101, 105
Morrall, Earl, 15, 20–21, 35, 101, 184
Morrison, Joe, 88
Moseley, Bill, 27

Namath, Joe, 122
NFL Championship games
  1929, 40
  1960, 60–65
  1961, 83 ff.
  1962, 19–20, 93–96
  1963, 101
  1965, 111–13
  1966, 139 ff.
  1967, 9 ff., 159 ff.
New York Giants, 16, 19–20, 52, 81 ff., 93–96, 134
Nitschke, Ray, 20, 86, 94, 96, 160, 186
Nobis, Tommy, 162
Nolan, Dick, 180
Norman, Pettis, 144

Oakland Raiders, 165–70
Orr, Jimmy, 156

Pace, Red, 136–37
Parilli, Vito, 28, 44, 47, 122
Peay, Francis, 173, 178
Percival, Mac, 177
Petitbon, Rich, 98
Philadelphia Eagles, 60–65, 145, 174
Pitts, Elijah, 98, 101, 141, 148, 151–52, 160, 166, 173
Play-action pass, 129
Plum, Milt, 15, 104
Pugh, Jethro, 11

Quarterbacking (Starr), 34, 121, 136
Quilan, Bill, 61

Rawhide Ranch, 117–18
Reeves, Dan, 144
Reichardt, Frederick, 41
Renfro, Mel, 141
Rentzel, Lance, 165
Riggle, Bob, 162
Ringo, Jimmy, 19, 79, 85
Roach, John, 99–100, 109
Robinson, Dave, 144, 160
Robustelli, Andy, 82
Rockne, Knute, 76
Ronzani, Gene, 40
Rote, Tobin, 43–44, 47
Rozelle, Pete, 97
Run to Daylight (Lombardi), 50, 70, 77
Ryan, Frank, 153

St. Louis Cardinals, 99
San Francisco 49ers, 51, 54, 58, 92–93, 103, 179–81
Schiffer, Don, 68
Schmidt, Joe, 15
Shinnick, Don, 75, 108
Sidney Lanier High School, 24, 27
Skoronski, Bob, 79, 85, 160, 184
Sport magazine, 20, 69, 118, 154, 170
Sports Illustrated, 157–58, 160
Starr, Bart
    birth and early childhood, 25 ff.
    characteristics as a quarterback, 15 ff.
    college ball, 31 ff.
    compared to Johnny Unitas, 156–58
    high school ball, 23–25, 27
    home life, 115 ff.
    influence of Lombardi, 73 ff.
    lifetime statistics, 187
    marriage, 43

Most Valuable Player, 154–55, 170
    quarterbacking tips, 121 ff.
    records, 13, 101, 104
    with Green Bay Packers, 41 ff.
Starr, Bart, Jr. (son), 115
Starr, Benjamin (father), 23, 25
Starr, Bret (son), 115
Starr, Cherry Morton (wife), 29, 43
Stram, Hank, 154
Super Bowl, 139 ff., 165–70
Szymanski, Dick, 35

Tarkenton, Fran, 15, 119–20, 153
Taylor, Jimmy, 17, 19–20, 51, 53, 56, 62–63, 68–69, 83, 86, 92–93, 95, 103, 105, 112, 131, 149, 155, 160
Taylor, Roosevelt, 98, 106, 161
Thurston, Fuzzy, 18, 79, 160, 184
Tittle, Y. A., 82 ff., 94, 184

Unitas, Johnny, 15, 81, 109, 153, 156–58, 184

Van Brocklin, Norm, 60–61, 63–64
Voris, Dick, 156

Wagner, Lee, 115–16
Walston, Bobby, 62
Washington Redskins, 179, 186
Weatherwax, Jim, 173, 175
Webster, Alex, 82
Whitsell, Dave, 98, 101
Whittenton, Jesse, 82
Whitworth, J. B., 34
Williams, Travis, 164, 173
Williamson, Fred, 149, 155
Wood, Willie, 151

Sport Shelf Books for Football Fans

Fran Tarkenton: The Scrambler
by Bill Libby

Bart Starr: The Cool Quarterback
by George Sullivan

The Glory Runners
by Al Hirshberg

Greatest Packers of Them All
by Chuck Johnson

Jim Brown: The Running Back
by Larry Klein

Joe Namath: A Football Legend
by David Lipman

The Johnny Unitas Story
by Lee Greene

The Pro Quarterbacks
by John Devaney

Pro Football's Unforgettable Games
by George Sullivan

Rockne of Notre Dame
by Delos W. Lovelace

The Author

George Sullivan has written a good-sized shelf of books and countless magazine articles as a full-time free-lance author. His other books for Putnam's include *Pro Football's Unforgettable Games, Touchdown,* and *Seven Wonders of the Modern World.* A former public relations manager and graduate of Fordham University, Mr. Sullivan lives with his wife and son in New York City.